Caring for Those in Crisis: Integrating Anthropology and Public Health in Complex Humanitarian Emergencies

■ Holly Ann Williams, ed.

napa bulletin   21

National Association for the Practice of Anthropology
A section of the American Anthropological Association

NAPA Bulletins are occasional publications of the National Association for the Practice of Anthropology, a section of the American Anthropological Association.

Dennis Wiedman and Linda Bennett
General Editors

Library of Congress Cataloging-in-Publication Data
Library of Congress Control Number: 2001135214

Napa 21 Bulletin—Caring for those in crisis: integrating anthropology and public health in complex humanitarian emergencies
Holly Ann Williams, ed.

ISBN 0-913303-01-0

www.NAPABulletin.org

Contents

CHAPTER 1

Caring for Those in Crisis: Integrating Anthropology and Public Health in Complex Humanitarian Emergencies

Holly Ann Williams
Malaria Epidemiology Branch, Division of Parasitic Diseases, National Center for Infectious Diseases, Centers for Disease Control and Prevention

Complex humanitarian emergencies (referred to in this bulletin as "complex emergencies"), defined as situations in which large civilian populations are exposed to war or civil strife, food shortages, and population displacement resulting in excess morbidity and mortality (Duffield 1994; Goodhand and Hulme 1999; Palmer and Zwi 1998; Roll Back Malaria 1999; Toole 1995), are an increasingly common problem throughout the world, most notably in Africa.[1] Complex emergencies compel humanitarian agencies from around the world to address the immediate and long-term needs of the affected populations. While the priority of humanitarian efforts during the acute phase is to save lives by meeting essential survival needs, understanding the larger sociocultural context of both the displacement experience and the complex emergency facilitates acceptance and effectiveness of public health interventions throughout the span of a complex emergency.[2]

This NAPA Bulletin addresses how and why anthropologists and health care practitioners should work together to better match humanitarian efforts to the needs of displaced populations, the specific geographic location and the phase of the emergency.[3] It is based on the premise that a multidisciplinary approach could best address the public health needs of a population in a complex emergency. A multidisciplinary approach not only helps meet the pressing public health needs of displaced populations, it also strengthens the effectiveness of the different professionals and their disciplines.

Complex Emergencies and the Challenge of Humanitarian Assistance

Complex emergencies are profoundly political processes. Complex emergencies may, in fact, be the objective of political or military strategies, rather than the consequence (Macrae and Zwi 1994; McClelland 2000; Young 1999). Similarly, humanitarian assistance is complex in its origins and effects, which may be a mix of philanthropy and politics (Middleton and O'Keefe 1998). While having to face not only the loss or disruption of familiar cultural systems, those displaced may be presented with the additional challenge of adjusting to the milieu in which humanitarian assistance is rendered. This political nature has ramifications for all persons involved—the displaced and host populations, as well as the staff of humanitarian agencies and the donor agencies and governments that support them. Aid that is meant to help can instead, at times, have a damaging impact (Anderson and Woodrow 1998; McClelland 2000; Nabeth et al. 1997; Slim 1997).

Globally, as the numbers of displaced persons continue to grow, the ability to address in an urgent manner the public health concerns of these populations can be a challenge for humanitarian relief agencies.[4] The sheer scale and complexity of some emergencies may stress the capacities of the nongovernmental organizations (NGO) attempting to respond to such situations. Most NGOs operate under tight fiscal constraints and find it difficult to field the staff needed to provide adequate health care. As well, NGO workers are not often experts in providing health care in complex emergencies, let alone have adequate training in cross-cultural sensitivities.

That being said, complex emergencies must be viewed with an understanding of which factors define how humanitarian assistance is rendered during a complex emergency and how those factors evolve. While some NGOs focus specifically on providing emergency relief aid, most NGOs focus generally on development. However, under emergency circumstances, NGOs focus often shifts from development to providing emergency humanitarian relief. One result of the loss of this development orientation is that refugees or other displaced persons become portrayed as "victims" rather than as active participants in their own destiny. Providing direct aid to victims may be perceived as quicker and more efficient than establishing programs that foster self-sufficiency or encourage active participation (Cromwell 1988; Médecins Sans Frontières 1997). Crisis conditions may mean that sound developmental approaches—informed analysis, sensitive implementation strategies and regular evaluations—are lost in the course of emergency responses (Anderson and Woodrow 1998).

When thousands upon thousands of displaced persons crowd into a common area of refuge in the group there are often many subpopulations, each with its own cultural identity and political and religious beliefs. At times, these subpopulations have a history of conflict with one another. For example,

in Sudan, where warring factions of Eritreans and Tigreans found themselves displaced together, and along the Thai/Cambodian border where
Khmer Rouge and Vietnamese soldiers fled to the same camps, it was
necessary for relief workers to understand the prior political context from
which these groups fled to minimize conflict within the region of refuge.
Within one large refugee camp on the Thai/Cambodian border, to provide
adequate protection to Vietnamese soldiers who had deserted the army
the living spaces of the Vietnamese had to be physically separate from the
Cambodian refugees, who viewed the deserted soldiers as a major threat
to the majority camp population. In camps in western Tanzania, Hutu-Tutsi
mixed-marriage refugees resided in a small, very well-protected camp to ensure their safety.

Large-scale displacements also tend to attract a great number of
NGOs, often with competing interests, operational philosophies and political agendas. Burkle describes the complex world of NGOs as "an international relief patchwork" (1995:38) with little structure. Frequently, there is
little communication or cooperation among these organizations and, as a
result, attempts to coordinate relief efforts in a manner acceptable to the
displaced populations often fail or are not fully successful.

The immediate needs of such large and complex populations often
preclude initial attention to anything other than ensuring basic survival.
The duration of the emergency is another factor to be considered. Acute
crises may extend temporally well beyond what one might expect and
evolve into long-standing situations that change intermittently as political
influences in the area shift or as military intervention or levels of violence
escalate. Southern Sudan is one example of a long-standing complex
emergency where the major humanitarian response to the situation, Operation Lifeline Sudan (OLS), has assisted for more than a decade. Settlements of Burmese refugees on the Thai/Myanmar border have been somewhat stable for the last decade, with fluctuations in the refugee population
reflecting levels of military action within Myanmar. Other long-standing
complex emergencies include the plight of Palestinians and the civil war in
Angola that has continued to produce both refugees and internally displaced persons for 40 years.

In a complex emergency, when the acute situation stabilizes and tran-
sitions to the postemergency phase, NGOs face different challenges as
they struggle to shift from emergency relief back to sustainable development. As NGOs address this transition and the resulting changes in public
health needs, their efforts are often complicated by limited or declining
budgets. As situations lengthen temporally, donor agencies may suffer
from "donor fatigue" and shift funds to newer, more urgent emergency situations in other countries. Alternatively, political tensions may accelerate
and dramatically alter the provision of supplies. For example, in March 2000,
staffs from 11 NGOs were evacuated from Southern Sudan in response to
an inability of the rebel leaders in the area, the Sudanese People's Liberation

Movement, United Nations' agencies and NGOs to agree on terms in a Memorandum of Agreement regarding humanitarian assistance. This was a major constraint for OLS as it altered its ability to provide adequate humanitarian assistance across all areas.

The Role of Anthropology in a Public Health Partnership

Given the global scope of complex emergencies, the often-frail political environment in which humanitarian assistance is provided, and the limited resources available to ameliorate such suffering, it is prudent to critically examine emergency public health responses. We must ask if there are different approaches that better address public health emergency needs in the wider sociopolitical context of the emergency situation.

Critically appraising the sociopolitical implications of the overall situation is essential to develop and successfully implement public health programs. Without an understanding of the events that culminated in the complex emergency, well-meaning efforts to address material needs of displaced populations might be misdirected or not be as effective.

An anthropological perspective has become increasingly recognized as a highly valuable contribution to improving medical care and public health (Coreil and Mull 1990; Hahn 1999; Heggenhougen 2000; Inhorn and Brown 1997).[5] However, applied anthropologists rarely have been teamed with public health practitioners in the arena of complex emergencies.

Anthropologists can offer a broader perspective on the events surrounding complex emergencies, and can assist in placing humanitarian efforts in the larger context of the lives of the displaced persons—lives that have had a history during the predisplacement and flight/displacement phases, and that continue long after the initial emergency period ends. Social scientists can also contribute valuable insights into areas previously given little attention: in particular, the economic, political, and social impacts on the host population from the humanitarian assistance provided, primarily in situations of self-settlement; and strategies employed by the affected populations in response to the local effects from assistance (Bakewell 2000; Waters 1999).

Although there is a long history of anthropologists contributing to refugee, migration, and displacement studies, most of this literature does not reflect anthropological field-based contributions to public health issues during a complex emergency. There is a dearth of literature describing the experiences of applied anthropologists in multidisciplinary teams responding to acute or chronic complex emergencies, particularly in the areas that might have most impact on the health of displaced populations: treatment seeking, compliance, access to and acceptance of health care, etc. A quick literature search using the key words of anthropology, social science, public health, refugees, and complex emergencies in *Current Contents for the Social and Behavioral Sciences* revealed 126 citations for the year 2000. The largest single grouping of the literature (44 citations, or 35 percent) focused on psychological sequela from displacement, mostly authored by psychologists or public health practitioners. The next-most frequent category of papers dealt with issues related to political analyses of the emergency or issues pertaining to law and human rights (33 citations, or 26 percent), again mostly, authored by nonanthropologists. Of the anthropology literature cited, reference to anthropological theory guiding research or intervention studies was lacking in almost all of the titles and abstracts.

As noted above, in the literature on refugees and displaced populations papers focusing on cultural influence on health were often written by nonanthropologists (Frye 1995; Nicholson and Kay 1999). Many papers are written on the psychological sequela of trauma and displacement, but did not consider the influence of culture on the interpretation of the trauma and the coping responses to that trauma (de Jong et al. 2000; Paardekooper et al. 1999). Noticeable exceptions to this pattern were papers that challenged the conventional biomedical approach to treating war trauma among refugees using verbalized expression of experience with an alternate approach that stressed the importance of nondiscursive bodily practices (Englund 1998), and one paper that examined the influence of culture and context on the pre- and postmigration experiences of refugee children (Rousseau et al. 1997). A recent trend in the literature was the call for attention to social and cultural aspects of complex emergencies. This, however, was not voiced by social scientists but by epidemiologists, nutritionists and physicians (Brundtland 2000; Burkle 1999; Davis 1996; Jaspars and Shoham 1999; Landman 1999; Webb and Harinarayan 1999).

Public health interventions could and should be strengthened by the application of social science knowledge from areas in which anthropologists have traditionally contributed: refugee studies, including issues pertinent to migration, displacement, and resettlement; sociopolitical resistance; social construction of belief systems, particularly after disasters; ethnomedicine; agricultural production strategies; household economics; famine and food security; cultural identity; restoration or innovation; race and ethnic relations; organizational conflict; reciprocity; policy development; and human rights (Bakewell 2000; Bloch et al. 2000; Bradbury 1998; Camino and Krulfeld 1994; Cernea 1999a, 1999b; Cernea and McDowell 2000; Colson 1971; Committee on Refugee Issues 1992–present; Englund 1998; Hansen 1979a, 1979b, 1990, 1994; Hansen and Oliver-Smith 1982; Harrell-Bond 1986; Hitchcox 1990; Indra 1999; Knudsen 1988; Krulfeld 1994; Long 1993; Oliver-Smith 1986; Oliver-Smith and Hoffman 1999; Reynell 1986; Sommers in press; Waters 1999; Williams 1990, 1993). Public health attention, particularly in the context of complex emergencies of increasing duration, now goes beyond the traditional areas of health and medical care to encompass issues relating to security, transportation, communication, and other aspects related to structural disruption (Burkle

1999). Given public health practitioners' shift in emphasis and the areas of displacement studies in which anthropologists engage, it seems a natural fit to work together in placing public health efforts within the wider social and cultural context surrounding and defining complex emergencies.

Linking Anthropology with Public Health

Public health practitioners can identify the most salient areas of public health needs (as defined by disease patterns) that require both short- and long-term programmatic support, as well as areas in which preventive measures might contribute to disease reduction given the constraints of a complex emergency situation. For example, epidemiologists use surveillance data to identify trends in morbidity and mortality. However, health information systems and surveillance data rarely incorporate sociocultural data to develop or modify health services and disease control programs in order to complement local health-related perceptions, values, and resources. Using complementary methods, anthropologists can also identify public health needs and help the affected population to articulate what they perceive as their needs. Anthropologists can also identify sociocultural determinants of health-related behaviors that are often lost in the stress of addressing the urgent needs of displaced populations. Using their historical approach to studying communities in depth, over time anthropologists are well situated to understand factors influencing the array of physical and mental health concerns that arise when situations shift from acute to chronic phases, or when displaced persons attempt to reintegrate into societies from which they previously had fled.

Although Chapter 6 of this bulletin discusses the progress made in incorporating cultural dimensions in training programs for humanitarian workers, medical and cultural anthropologists should take a more proactive role in highlighting existing knowledge about various populations in crisis. As early as the 1980s, some epidemiologists working in the field of complex emergencies recognized the need for incorporating sociocultural knowledge into public health practice, both operationally and in the areas of staff training (Dick and Simmonds 1983). The question is raised: What sources of sociocultural knowledge could be utilized? One idea would be to use previously published ethnographies about communities that later become displaced as reference material for international humanitarian workers. The ethnographies would be useful in describing cultural practices and what constituted "normal" behavior before the crisis.

Little information exists on how the social context of a complex emergency might affect levels of morbidity and mortality. Given the mandate to control the often devastating implications of communicable and chronic diseases in displaced populations, it is not surprising that the attention of public health and health care practitioners is not focused on the broader context. Public health decisions should not be made in a sociopolitical vacuum, but rather from an informed position that has carefully considered the perceptions and needs of the affected community, and incorporating both the displaced and host communities.

As mentioned earlier, complex emergencies are profoundly political processes, and a key feature has become the lengthy duration of many of these "emergencies." It is critical that a wider array of political, social, and economic information be given to NGOs who must work under these difficult conditions—for example, the impact of political instability on the security of the host population, on the tenure of the displaced population, and on the abilities of NGOs to carry out their functions (Burkle 1995). As well, attention to the social context of a complex emergency will be crucial in making appropriate decisions regarding what and how assistance should be provided (Palmer and Zwi 1998). Anthropologists can play a pivotal role in assisting these practitioners to achieve this broader view. They are also in an ideal position to go beyond interpreting culture to actually advocating the need for a community voice that truly represents those affected by the complex emergency.

Cernea (1999b) strongly argues that social organization offers a frame of reference for addressing specific problems, one that is often missing from the perspectives of technical colleagues. He stresses that an examination of social organization should serve as the conceptual foundation and starting point for applied anthropology work. Applied anthropologists could study the social organization of displaced populations to identify linkages and dependencies, illuminate alternate meaning systems and identify all possible social actors who might have a stake in the problem under analysis.

For example, reproductive health needs for women, particularly in regard to gender-based violence, are beginning to be recognized as an important area in complex emergencies; however, much still needs to be done to enhance the provision of reproductive health services (Palmer et al. 1999). In terms of displaced populations, social science research has primarily focused on the chronic phase of a complex emergency or during resettlement. Anthropologists can and should contribute to this area by clarifying women's perspectives, advocating for health policy in this area and contributing to information, education and communication messages by interpreting social, cultural, environmental and economic conditions that might influence the acceptance of various interventions.[6] Kulig's (1994) work on how role changes for resettled Cambodian women affected childbearing interests and family planning is a good example of this.

Mental health issues related to complex emergencies are another public health area to which social scientists could meaningfully contribute. Violence and fear created by violence are common features of many complex emergencies. Actual violence or the fear of continued threats may permeate the daily lives of displaced persons, even up to and beyond the time of repatriation or resettlement. Anthropologists can help analyze the effects of violence from a community or societal perspective, rather than examining individual clinical responses to the violence, and can assist public health practitioners to redefine the concept of "normality" in such situations. Questions such as "What is a healthy way of acting in a refugee camp?" or "To what extent do traditional notions of well-being apply in situations of extreme distress?" (Desjarlais et al. 1995:133) have been posed by researchers in social medicine. Ethnographic methods could provide data that would help to inform these issues. As well, therapeutic interventions for dealing with violence should address cultural and individual needs in order to help reestablish a sense of security in everyday lives.

Qualitative Methods Most Applicable to Complex Emergency Situations

A wide array of anthropological methods may be employed to enhance the Knowledge, Attitudes, and Practices (KAP) survey method, commonly used by epidemiologists in the field. The KAP survey is often used as a proxy to gather "qualitative" data when, in reality, much of the data that are collected with this method are quantitative. Anthropologists have used different methods when doing refugee research—systematically collecting data that combine qualitative and quantitative approaches and/or the more traditional, interpretive-reflexive, and qualitative approach (Krulfeld 1994). A few techniques that could strengthen the development, introduction, acceptance and sustainability of public health interventions are participant observation, individual and focus group interviews, collection of life histories, discourse analysis, free listing, ranking, pile sorts, multidimensional scaling techniques, risk or needs assessments, household livelihood and household vulnerability surveys, and nutritional/anthropometry surveys. In terms of multidisciplinary teamwork in public health, incorporating both qualitative and quantitative methods is often appreciated, and strengthens the approach. For a thorough discussion of the benefits of integrating both qualitative and quantitative research methods, see Bamberger (2000b) and Hentschel (1999). A recent World Bank publication (Bamberger 2000a) includes a series of development-oriented case studies that demonstrate the utility of mixed-methods approaches.

Rapid ethnographic assessments (also called rapid assessment procedures [RAP], rapid community assessments, or rapid and participatory rural appraisals) are methods appropriate to use in the context of a complex emergency. While having origins in agricultural and farming systems research and rapid rural appraisal, RAP, when applied to public health problems, uses group-based and individual ethnographic methods to gather cultural, social, economic, and behavioral data in a timely fashion. These form the basis for more in-depth investigation of health problems, or help design culturally appropriate prevention or intervention programs. A central concept of RAP is the inclusion of the affected community in the processes of data collection, analysis and problem solving. It stresses the viewpoint of the displaced community as opposed to that of the humanitar-ian worker or agency perspective (Harris et al. 1997; Weiss et al. 2000). The Center for Refugee and Disaster Studies at The Johns Hopkins Univer-sity School of Public Health is developing a RAP guide specifically geared to understanding the perceived needs of refugees and internally dis-placed persons, and is a good reference to use while conducting field work (Weiss et al. 2000).[7]

Application of Theory to Practice

This bulletin strongly reflects field-oriented practice; however, prac-tice and theory should not be separate. That said, the reality is, as Wald-man and Williams note in Chapter 6 of this bulletin, that the discipline of refugee health is new and not yet a science. In *NAPA Bulletin 18*, Hill (2000) compares the processes of traditional and applied research. The objective and expected outcome of applied research is the application of problem solving to alleviate some type of human misery or injustice. Prac-titioners of any discipline involved in refugee health are at the early stages of trying to describe the "standard" current approaches being used, evalu-ate the utility of previous approaches, formulate pressing questions that need to be answered, identify the data that can best answer those ques-tions, and how to gather such data and then test novel interventions that might be applied. Institutional systems of monitoring and evaluation are not yet in place, nor has there been a critical appraisal of the knowledge generated from the field over the years to determine how to best advance the development of theory. With the accumulation of fundamental knowl-edge about complex emergencies comes the building of theory, a set of ideas that explain. Baba (2000:36) presents the theory building process as a spiral of new knowledge where theory and practice are interdependent elements. The beginning of this spiral is when a societal problem or ques-tion is identified that calls for disciplined inquiry, such as when the anthro-pologist is dispatched to a refugee camp to understand problems of gen-der relations. As this problem-oriented research occurs in new field of investigation, it yields basic information that provides a foundation for the development and further refinement of theoretical knowledge. The emerg-ing body of theory is then drawn upon to investigate and solve other prob-lems in related domains; for example, in providing culturally appropriate health care to women in refugee camp clinics. Finally, as professional practitioners continue to push out into new contexts beyond what is known about complex emergencies, they again fundamentally generate new knowledge that informs and develops theory. Viewed in this way, practice is coequal to theory in the process of knowledge creation; theory and prac-tice exist in a mutually causal relationship. The theory of practice for refugee health is emerging, and this bulletin strives to contribute to that development.

Proponents of a critical medical anthropology urge medical anthropologists to examine the sociomedical context in which it has emerged (Baer et al. 1986). It is necessary to move beyond just comparing medical systems. The political economy of health should also be considered; this includes examining institutional, national, and global level influences (Morsy 1996). This is particularly important in the context of complex emergencies, where little attention has been given to how those forces impact the provision of health services. As has been noted, public health practitioners can no longer concentrate on providing immediate humanitarian care without a recognition and an understanding of the macro-level forces that shape what type of aid is considered appropriate, the amount of aid that is given and the conditions under which relief agencies may operate. Ignoring these political forces is at best naïve and may, in fact, contribute to the inability of NGOs to deliver care. Attention to the political economy of health within the constraints imposed by the nature of complex emergencies is an area in which social scientists can make a valuable contribution. In a recent paper (Porter et al. 1999), public health practitioners are also urged to move beyond a narrow biological perspective of infectious disease control to developing an "infectious disease policy." As with the political economy of health, this stresses a process oriented policy approach that encompasses an understanding of obstacles such as poverty, inequality, environmental factors and the interrelationship between communities and individuals as they interact with the health care system. The end result would be a "process of change—change in orientation, in vision, in practice and in purpose" (Porter et al. 1999:322).

This bulletin argues that, by combining their individual perspectives and disciplinary strengths, public health practitioners and social scientists could use their wider understanding of how humanitarian health care is provided, noting both limitations and opportunities, to pave the way for improved practice within the new discipline of refugee health. Ultimately, this should enhance theory development.

Contributions to this Bulletin

Bulletin 21 is a collection of articles that address different dimensions of integrating epidemiology and anthropology in the situation of a complex emergency. The authors represent applied practitioners, either in anthropology and/or epidemiology, all of whom have field experience with refugees or displaced persons. Collectively, these papers offer practical examples of multidisciplinary approaches that could be used in all phases of a complex emergency to strengthen the provision of adequate public health services. This is an attempt to answer the call from other disciplines for more social science input to public health challenges in complex emergencies.

Fustukian and Zwi begin this bulletin by challenging the standard approach to public health in a complex emergency, that of a medicalized disaster response, and urge, rather, that a broader social approach encompassing the viewpoints of the displaced population be used. McSpadden and MacArthur provide an analysis of critical human rights concerns that arise when outside intervention is provided in a complex emergency. MacArthur, Dudley, and Williams offer a case study of a refugee situation in which public health practitioners used community-based approaches tailored to the differing cultural backgrounds of a displaced population. Williams and Bloland argue that, although research is definitely needed and valid in the context of a complex emergency, several practical issues need to be addressed in order for a research program to be successful. Lastly, Waldman and Williams discuss "lessons learned": What do we know from field experiences and what do we need to do better? As Zwi et al. (1999) noted, it is time that the efforts of public health and humanitarian assistance be examined to determine their contributions and limits in reestablishing lives, promoting health, and building peace.[8]

Notes

Disclaimer. The views expressed within this chapter are solely of the authors and do not reflect those of the United States Public Health Service.

1. A common method of defining a public health "emergency" that requires humanitarian assistance is to use epidemiologic terms: situations in which mortality rates exceed 1/10,000 population per day. The broader term, *complex humanitarian emergency,* is a descriptive category that defines some of the conditions that create the public health emergency. Some definitions also include displacement related to natural disasters, although for the purpose of this bulletin, we will be focusing discussion on complex emergencies not related to natural disasters. For a comparison of the features of complex and noncomplex emergencies, see Burkle 1995:40.

2. Complex emergencies are conceptualized as having at least two stages, each with differing needs. The emergency phase is described as in note #1, with a drop in mortality below 1/10,000 population per day signaling the postemergency or chronic phase. Some practitioners refer to the chronic phase as the time when the nature of the relief effort shifts from emergency to development in nature. However, the terms used to describe the phases, as well as the definitions of those terms, are not universally agreed upon within and/or among the various disciplines engaged in offering humanitarian assistance.

3. Although the term *anthropologist* is used often in the text, we recognize that there are other social scientists who receive similar training in research methodologies and who could contribute to improving the public health needs of the displaced. That being said, the anthropological training imparts a specific way of examining culture that is not generally a component of the training of other social scientists. However, throughout the various chapters, we will interchange the term *anthropologist* with *social scientist* in an effort to broadly recognize both the expertise and interests of others who can play a significant role in improving services to displaced populations.

4. For the purposes of this bulletin, humanitarian relief agencies can include international and national or local nongovernmental organizations (NGO), the various United Nations programs relating to relief, private voluntary organizations, and host government agencies that provide health care services to displaced populations.

5. In addition to texts that specifically link anthropology to public health, general information about things like perceptions of disease causation and healing or treatment seeking behaviors can be extrapolated to populations suffering in complex emergency situations. While a discussion of medical anthropology in general is beyond the scope of this chapter, the following references illustrate a sampling of the variety that exists within the medical

anthropology literature (Feierman and Janzen 1992; Green 1999; Janzen 1978; Kleinman 1980; Sargent and Johnson 1996; and Van Der Geest and Whyte 1988).

6. IECs are commonly used in public health programs to promote health education messages or to gain acceptance of new public health messages. They are designed as participatory approach methods that rely on the notion that education empowers people to make decisions, modify behaviors and change social conditions (UNHCR 1999).

7. Although it is beyond the scope of this bulletin to discuss in detail individual methods, for further reading on RAP see Beebe 1995; Chambers 1992; Cornwall and Jewkes 1995; David, Zakus and Lysack 1998; Leurs 1997; Manderson and Aaby 1992; Ngunjiri 1998; Nichter 1999; and Rifkin 1996. Guha–Sapir (1991) offers a review of rapid assessments in mass emergencies from an epidemiologic perspective.

8. For an excellent critique of how certain principles of development work are lost during the perceived urgency of a crisis, I refer readers to *Rising from the Ashes: Development Strategies in Times of Disaster* (Anderson and Woodrow 1998). Using case studies gathered in the International Relief/Development Project, the book examines lessons learned from international NGOs and provides an analytical framework for analyzing capacities and vulnerabilities. The purpose of the book is, as the authors describe, "to help the givers of aid learn how to give it so that it supports the efforts of people to achieve social and economic development" (Anderson and Woodrow 1998:1).

References Cited

Anderson, Mary, and Peter Woodrow
    1998 Rising from the Ashes: Development Strategies in Times of Disaster. Boulder: Westview Press.
Baba, Marietta L.
    2000 Theories of Practice in Anthropology: A Critical Appraisal. *In* The Unity of Theory and Practice in Anthropology: Rebuilding a Fractured Synthesis. NAPA Bulletin 18. Carole E. Hill and Marietta L. Baba, eds. Pp. 17–44. Washington, DC: American Anthropological Association.
Baer, Hans, Merrill Singer, and John H. Johnsen
    1986 Toward a Critical Medical Anthropology. Social Science and Medicine 23:95–98.
Bakewell, Oliver
    2000 Uncovering Local Perspectives on Humanitarian Assistance and Its Outcomes. Disasters 24:103–116.
Bamberger, Michael
    2000a Opportunities and Challenges for Integrating Quantitative and Qualitative Research. *In* Integrating Quantitative and Qualitative Research in Development Projects, Michael Bamberger, ed. Pp. 3–36. Washington, DC: The World Bank.
    2000b Integrating Quantitative and Qualitative Research in Development Projects. Washington, DC: The World Bank.
Beebe, James
    1995 Basic Concepts and Techniques of Rapid Appraisal. Human Organization 53:42–51.
Bloch, Alice, Treasa Galvin, and Barbara Harrell-Bond
    2000 Refugee Women in Europe: Some Aspects of the Legal and Policy Dimensions. International Migration 38:169–188.
Bradbury, Mark
    1998 Normalising the Crisis in Africa. Disasters 22:328–338.
Brundtland, Gro Harlem
    2000 Editorial. Mental Health of Refugees, Internally Displaced Persons and Other Populations Affected by Conflict. Acta Psychiatry Scandanavia 102:159–161.
Burkle, Frederick M.
    1995 Complex, Humanitarian Emergencies: I. Concepts and Participants. Prehospital and Disaster Medicine 10:36–42.
    1999 Fortnightly Review. Lessons Learnt and Future Expectations of Complex Emergencies. British Medical Journal 319:422–426.
Camino, Linda, and Ruth Krulfeld, eds.
    1994 Reconstructing Lives, Recapturing Meaning. Refugee Identity, Gender, and Culture Change. Amsterdam: Gordon and Breach Publishers.

Cernea, Michael, ed.
    1999a The Economics of Involuntary Resettlement. Questions and Challenges. Wash-
        ington, DC: The World Bank.
    1999b Malinowski Award Lecture. Social Organization and Development Anthropology.
        Human Organization 54:340–352.
Cernea, Michael, and Christopher McDowell, eds.
    2000 Risks and Reconstruction. Experiences of Resettlers and Refugees. Washington,
        DC: The World Bank.
Chambers, Robert
    1992 Rural Appraisal: Rapid, Relaxed and Participatory. Institute of Development Stud-
        ies. Discussion Paper, 311. Brighton, UK: University of Sussex.
Colson, Elizabeth
    1971 The Social Consequences of Resettlement. Manchester, UK: University of Man-
        chester.
Committee on Refugee Issues
    1992-present Selected Papers on Refugee Issues. Washington, DC: American Anthro-
        pological Association.
Coreil, Jeannine, and J. Dennis Mull
    1990 Anthropology and Primary Health Care. Boulder: Westview Press.
Cornwall, Andrea and Rachel Jewkes
    1995 What Is Participatory Research? Social Science and Medicine 41:1667–1676.
Cromwell, Godfrey
    1988 Field Report. Note on the Role of Expatriate Administrators in Agency-Assisted
        Refugee Programmes. Journal of Refugee Studies 1:297–307.
David, J., L. Zakus, and Catherine L. Lysack
    1998 Review Article. Revisiting Community Participation. Health Policy and Planning
        13:1–12.
Davis, Austen P.
    1996 Targeting the Vulnerable in Emergency Situations: Who Is Vulnerable? The Lancet
        348:868–871.
de Jong, J. P., W. F. Scholte, M. W. J. Koeter, and A. A. M. Hart
    2000 The Prevalence of Mental Health Problems in Rwandan and Burundese Refugee
        Camps. Acta Psychiatry Scandanavia 102:171–177.
Desjarlais, Robert, Leon Eisenberg, Byron Good, and Arthur Kleinman
    1995 World Mental Health: Problems and Priorities in Low-Income Countries. New York:
        Oxford University Press.
Dick, Bruce, and Stephanie Simmonds
    1983 Refugee Health Care: Similar but Different? Disasters 7:291–303.
Duffield, Mark
    1994 The Political Economy of Internal War: Asset Transfer, Complex Emergencies and
        International Aid. In War and Hunger: Rethinking International Responses to Complex
        Emergencies. Joanna Macrae and Anthony Zwi, eds., with Mark Duffield and Hugo
        Slim. Pp. 50–69. London: Zed Books.
Englund, Harri
    1998 Death, Trauma and Ritual: Mozambican Refugees in Malawi. Social Science and
        Medicine 46:1165–1174.
Feierman, Steven, and John M. Janzen, eds.
    1992 The Social Basis of Health and Healing in Africa. Berkeley: University of California
        Press.
Frye, Barbara A.
    1995 Use of Cultural Themes in Promoting Health among Southeast Asian Refugees.
        American Journal of Health Promotion 9:269–280.
Goodhand, Jonathon, and David Hulme
    1999 From Wars to Complex Political Emergencies: Understanding Conflict and Peace-
        Building in the New World Disorder. Third World Quarterly 20:13–26.
Green, Edward C.
    1999 Indigenous Theories of Contagious Disease. Walnut Creek, CA: AltaMira Press.
Guha-Sapir, Debarati
    1991 Rapid Assessment of Health Needs in Mass Emergencies: Review of Current Con-
        cepts and Methods. World Health Statistical Quarterly 44:171–181.

Hahn, Robert A., ed., with Kate W. Harris
  1999   Anthropology in Public Health. Bridging Differences in Culture and Society. New York: Oxford University Press.
Hansen, Art
  1979a   Managing Refugees: Zambia's Response to Angolan Refugees 1996–1977. Disasters 3:374–380.
  1979b   Once the Running Stops: Assimilation of Angolan Refugees into Zambian Border Villages. Disasters 3:369–374.
  1990   Refugee Self-Settlement versus Settlement on Government Schemes. United Nations Research Institute for Social Development Discussion Paper 17. Geneva: United Nations.
  1994   The Illusion of Local Sustainability and Self-Sufficiency: Famine in a Border Area of North-Western Zambia. Human Organization 53:11–20.
Hansen, Art, and Anthony Oliver-Smith, eds.
  1982   Involuntary Migration and Resettlement. The Problems and Responses of Dislocated People. Boulder: Westview Press.
Harrell-Bond, Barbara
  1986   Imposing Aid. Emergency Assistance to Refugees. Oxford: Oxford University Press.
Harris, Kari Jo, Norge W. Jerome, and Stephen B. Fawcett
  1997   Commentary. Rapid Assessment Procedures: A Review and Critique. Human Organization 56:375–378.
Heggenhougen, H. Kris
  2000   More Than Just "Interesting!" Anthropology, Health and Human Rights. Social Science and Medicine 50:1171–1175.
Hentschel, Jesko
  1999   Contextuality and Data Collection Methods: A Framework and Application to Health Service Utilisation. The Journal of Development Studies 35:64–94.
Hill, Carole E.
  2000   Strategic Issues for Rebuilding a Theory and Practice Synthesis. In The Unity of Theory and Practice in Anthropology: Rebuilding a Fractured Synthesis. NAPA Bulletin 18. Carole E. Hill and Marietta L. Baba, eds. Pp. 1–16. Washington, DC: American Anthropological Association.
Hitchcox, Linda
  1990   Vietnamese Refugees in Southeast Asian Camps. Oxford: Macmillion.
Indra, Doreen, ed.
  1999   Engendering Forced Migration: Theory and Practice (Refugee and Forced Migration Studies, vol. 5). New York: Berghahn Books.
Inhorn, Marcia C., and Peter J. Brown, eds.
  1997   The Anthropology of Infectious Disease: International Health Perspectives. Theory and Practice in Medical Anthropology and International Health, No. 4. Amsterdam: Gordon and Breach Science Publishers.
Janzen, John M., with Williams Arkinstall
  1978   The Quest for Therapy: Medical Pluralism in Lower Zaire. Berkeley: University of California Press.
Jaspars, Suzanne, and Jeremy Shoham
  1999   Targeting the Vulnerable: A Review of the Necessity and Feasibility of Targeting Vulnerable Households. Disasters 23:359–372.
Kleinman, Arthur
  1980   Patients and Healers in the Context of Culture: An Exploration of the Borderland between Anthropology, Medicine, and Psychiatry. Comparative Studies of Health Systems and Medical Care, no. 3. Berkeley: University of California Press.
Knudsen, J.
  1988   Vietnamese Survivors: Process Involved in Refugee Coping and Adaptation. Bergen, Norway: Department of Social Anthropology, University of Bergen.
Krulfeld, Ruth
  1994   Methods in Refugee Research: Two Ethnographic Approaches. In Reconstructing Lives, Recapturing Meaning: Refugee Identity, Gender and Culture Change. Linda Camino and Ruth Krufeld, eds. Pp. 147–150. Amsterdam: Gordon and Breach Publishers.

Kulig, Judith
  1994   Old Traditions in a New World: Changing Gender Relations Among Cambodian
     Refugees. *In* Reconstructing Lives, Recapturing Meaning: Refugee Identity, Gender
     and Culture Change. Linda Camino and Ruth Krufeld, eds. Pp. 129–148. Amsterdam:
     Gordon and Breach Publishers.
Landman, Jacqueline
  1999   Food Aid in Emergencies: A Case for Wheat? Proceedings of the Nutritional Soci-
     ety 58:355–361.
Leurs, Robert
  1997   Critical Reflections on Rapid and Participatory Rural Appraisal. Development in
     Practice 7:291–293.
Long, Lynette
  1993   Ban Vinai. The Refugee Camp. New York: Columbia University Press.
Macrae, Joanna, and Anthony Zwi
  1994   Famine, Complex Emergencies and International Policy in Africa: An Overview. *In*
     War and Hunger: Rethinking International Responses to Complex Emergencies.
     Joanna Macrae and Anthony Zwi, eds., with Mark Duffield and Hugo Slim. Pp. 6–36.
     London: Zed Books.
Manderson, Lenore A. and Peter Aaby
  1992   Can Rapid Anthropological Procedures be Applied to Tropical Disease? Health
     Policy and Planning 7:46–55.
Médecins Sans Frontières
  1997   Refugee Health: An Approach to Emergency Situations. London: Macmillan.
McClelland, Donald G., with Elizabeth Adelsko, Richard Hill, John Mason, and Robert Muscat
  2000   Complex Humanitarian Emergencies and USAID's Humanitarian Response.
     USAID Program and Operations Assessment Report No. 27. Washington, DC: Center
     for Development Information and Evaluation, USAID.
Middleton, Neil, and Phil O'Keefe
  1998   Disaster and Development. The Politics of Humanitarian Aid. London: Pluto Press.
Morsy, Soheir A.
  1996   Political Economy in Medical Anthropology. *In* Medical Anthropology: Contempo-
     rary Theory and Method. Revised Edition. Carolyn F. Sargent and Thomas M. Johnson,
     eds. Pp. 21–40. Westport, CT: Praeger.
Nabeth, Pierre, Brigitte Vasset, Philippe Guérin, Brigitte Doppler, and Milton Tectonidis
  1997   Health Situation of Refugees in Eastern Zaire. The Lancet 349:1031–1032.
Ngunjiri, Eliud
  1998   Participatory Methodologies: Double-Edged Swords. Development in Practice 8:
     466–470.
Nicholson, Barbara L., and Diane M. Kay
  1999   Group Treatment of Traumatized Cambodian Women: A Culture-Specific Ap-
     proach. Social Work 44:470–479.
Nichter, Mark
  1999   Project Community Diagnosis: Participatory Research as a First Step toward Com-
     munity Involvement in Primary Health Care. *In* Anthropology in Public Health: Bridging
     Differences in Culture and Society. Robert Hahn, ed. Pp. 300–324. New York: Oxford
     University Press.
Oliver-Smith, Anthony
  1986   The Martyred City. Death and Rebirth in the Andes. Albuquerque: University of
     New Mexico Press.
Oliver-Smith, Anthony, and Susanna M. Hoffman
  1999   The Angry Earth: Disaster in Anthropological Perspective. NY: Routledge.
Paardekooper, B., J. T. V. M. de Jong, and J. M. A. Hermanns
  1999   The Psychological Impact of War and the Refugee Situation on South Sudanese
     Children in Refugee Camps in Northern Uganda: An Exploratory Study. Journal of Child
     Psychology and Psychiatry 40:529–536.
Palmer, Celia, Louisiana Lush, and Anthony Zwi
  1999   The Emerging International Policy Agenda for Reproductive Health Services in
     Conflict Settings. Social Science and Medicine 49:1689–1703.
Palmer, Celia, and Anthony Zwi
  1998   Women, Health and Humanitarian Aid in Conflict. Disasters 22:236–249.

Porter, John, Jessica Odgen, and Paul Pronyk
    1999 Infectious Disease Policy: Towards the Production of Health. Health Policy and Planning 14:322–328.
Reynell, Josephine
    1986 Socio-Economic Evaluation of the Khmer Camps on the Thai-Kampuchean Border. Oxford: Refugee Studies Programme.
Rifkin, Susan B.
    1996 Rapid Rural Appraisal: Its Use and Value for Health Planners and Managers. Public Administration 74:509–526.
Roll Back Malaria Technical Support Network on Malaria Control in Complex Emergencies
(Dr. M. Connolly, Manager)
    1999 Background and Terms of Reference. Unpublished document. Roll Back Malaria Technical Support Network.
Rousseau, Cecile, Aline Drapeau, and Ellen Corin
    1997 The Influence of Culture and Context on the Pre- and Post-Migration Experience of School-Aged Refugees from Central America and Southeast Asia in Canada. Social Science and Medicine 44:1115–1127.
Sargent, Carolyn F., and Thomas M. Johnson, eds.
    1996 Medical Anthropology: Contemporary Theory and Method. Revised Edition. Westport, CT: Greenwood Publishing Group, Inc.
Slim, Hugo
    1997 Doing the Right Thing: Relief Agencies, Moral Dilemmas and Moral Responsibility in Political Emergencies and War. Disasters 21:244–257.
Sommers, Marc
    In press Fear in Bongoland: Burundi Refugees in Urban Tanzania. New York: Berghahn Books, Inc.
Toole, Michael
    1995 Mass Population Displacement: A Global Public Health Challenge. Infectious Disease Clinics of North America 9:353–365.
United Nations High Commissioner for Refugees
    1999 Reproductive Health in Refugee Situations: An Interagency Field Manual. Geneva: UNHCR.
Van der Geest, Sjaak, and Susan Reynolds Whyte, eds.
    1988 The Context of Medicine in Developing Countries. Dordrecht: the Netherlands: Kluwer Academic Publishers.
Waters, Tony
    1999 Assessing the Impact of the Rwandan Refugee Crisis on Development Planning in Rural Tanzania, 1994–1996. Human Organization 58:142–152.
Webb, Patrick, and Anuradha Harinarayan
    1999 A Measure of Uncertaintly: The Nature of Vulnerability and Its Relationship to Malnutrition. Disasters 23:292–305.
Weiss, William M., Paul Bolton, and Anita V. Shankar
    2000 Rapid Assessment Procedures (RAP). A Guide to Understanding the Perceived Needs of Refugees and Internally Displaced Populations. Unpublished draft, January 2000.
Williams, Holly Ann
    1990 Families in Refugee Camps. Human Organization 49:100–109.
    1993 Self-Settled Refugees in North–Western Zambia: Shifting Norms of Assistance from Social Networks. In Selected Papers on Refugee Issues: II. Mary Carol Hopkins and Nancy D. Donnelly, eds. Pp. 135–155. Washington, DC: American Anthropological Association.
Young, Helen
    1999 Public Nutrition in Emergencies: An Overview of Debates, Dilemmas and Decision-Making. Disasters 23:277–291.
Zwi, Anthony, Suzanne Fustukian, and Dinesh Sethi
    1999 Never Again, Once Again: Learning from the Kosovan Tragedy. European Journal of Public Health 9:81–82.

CHAPTER 2

Balancing Imbalances: Facilitating Community Perspectives in Times of Adversity

Suzanne Fustukian
Centre for International Health Studies, Queen Margaret University College

Anthony B. Zwi
Health Policy Unit, London School of Hygiene and Tropical Medicine

In recent years, public health debates have increasingly acknowledged the critical importance of understanding the context of people's lives and the integral impact this has on health and should have on influencing health sector response (Baum 1995; Lee and Paxman 1997). An appreciation of context goes beyond seeking to address essential public health needs—adequate sanitation and clean water, sufficient food of good quality, adequate shelter, and the prevention and control of epidemics and the spread of disease—considered the first priorities in the public health response to complex humanitarian emergencies (CHE). This chapter argues that although meeting basic needs is essential in these situations, attention to power and resource imbalances are equally fundamental to promoting public health. Understanding power and resource imbalances helps to elucidate the differential experience of vulnerability, marginalization and inequity among conflict affected populations. Such concerns are embodied in a "social model of health," which asserts that health is produced "not just by individual biology and medical intervention, but by conditions in the wider natural, social, economic, and political environment" (Jones 1994:12) and by individual, family, community, and institutional responses to these multiple environments.

To what extent are these broader contextual concerns reflected in the public health responses to complex emergencies? And to what extent are these concerns valid in situations in which survival itself—both for the individual and the population group—is often at stake? Is the dominant public health approach to emergencies, which prioritizes basic human needs and saving lives through a medicalized disaster response, more appropriate to the needs of war-displaced populations than a process-oriented approach that seeks to engage with the displaced population in jointly developing strategies for health improvement? Is it possible for both approaches to be incorporated in a more process- and context-sensitive approach? And, if possible, how feasible is it to engage communities when they have been shattered by external events and experiences of conflict? These and related questions will be explored in this article. We begin by describing the current discourse of public health in humanitarian crises, and then consider in greater detail issues related to emergency public health.

The Discourse on Complex Humanitarian Emergencies

Since the early 1990s, when the concept of CHEs first emerged (Bok 1999; Duffield 1994a), the discourse around CHEs has drawn increasingly on perspectives from a number of disciplines: political economy, political science, international relations, anthropology, public health, development studies, human rights, peace studies, and economics. Conflict and CHEs are typically viewed by these disciplines from either "macro" or "micro" perspectives; both perspectives are required to appreciate fully the complexity of the CHE and to devise appropriate and effective responses. Goodhand and Hulme (1999) argue, for example, that it is important, first and foremost, to recognize conflict as a "social" process rather than an "event" with a precise beginning and end. This process reflects responses to a particular "configuration of power, structures, actors and beliefs or grievances" (1999:17). In order to understand such a process, "detailed contextual analysis and an exploration of the local dynamics of CPEs [Complex Political Emergencies]" (1999:17) is needed. From a political economy perspective, Duffield argues that complex emergencies are deeply politicized conflicts "characteristic of areas of protracted economic crisis and growing social vulnerability" (1994b:50), actively marginalized by the global economy and in which "violence has become an important adjunct of economic and political survival in landscapes increasingly lacking alternatives" (Duffield 1994a:38). Unlike earlier conflicts, which were associated with "state formation," the current phase of global insecurity reflects "state disintegration," suggests Cliffe and Luckham (1999), Duffield (1994a), and Kaldor (1993).

Although acknowledging the unique characteristics of each CHE, common features can be identified. Goodhand and Hulme (1999) suggest five: (1) conflict within and across state boundaries; (2) political origins; (3) protracted duration (i.e., before and after the so-called emergency, society exhibits heightened levels of physical and psychosocial violence); (4) social cleavages (often around unequal access to political institutions and economic activity); and (5) predatory social formations, often predicated on ethnonationalist groupings that are "mobilised and manipulated by conflict entrepreneurs and political opportunists" (1999:17). Leaning (1999) identifies four characteristic outcomes of CHEs: massive "population dislocation; destruction of social networks and ecosystems; insecurity of civilians and non-combatants; and human rights abuses" (1999:6). In addition, the destruction of roads, health facilities, and other infrastructure, or the presence of land mines may deter access to isolated communities or disable supply routes from reaching areas of need (World Health Organization 1999; Zwi 1996). The combination of these outcomes has presented immense challenges to relief agencies.

Humanitarian assistance, mobilized in response to CHEs, is often triggered by substantial human rights abuses within countries and/or major cross-border population movements into neighboring states as occurred in Rwanda (Jean 1995) and Kosovo (Zwi et al. 1999) or, increasingly, within the borders of a state as in Sudan (Jok 1998; Levine 1997) or East Timor (Aglionby and Zinn 1999). In each of these situations, forced migration was triggered by a key event and the response to the event: genocide in Rwanda; ethnic repression and then NATO bombing in Serbia; the referendum and reactionary response to it in East Timor. In recent years, over 50 million people worldwide have been forced to flee their homes, and often their countries, in order to seek safety and refuge (Reed et al. 1998; Zetter 1999). Global estimates of refugee numbers have reached approximately 20 million, with many more, perhaps up to 30 million, internally displaced (Schmeidl 1998; Zetter 1999).

The "Emergency Paradigm"

Emergency public health typically divides emergencies into two discrete phases: acute and postemergency (Banatvala et al. 1999; Hanquet 1997). The objectives of the acute emergency phase are to reduce death and illness from preventable causes and starvation. One of the key benchmarks for management during a crisis is the capacity of relief and host health services to reduce the daily crude mortality rate (CMR) from very high levels to those comparable to the host population or the affected population prior to the conflict. Compared with nonemergency CMR thresholds, which may average between 12–20 per 1,000 per annum in developing countries (equivalent to 0.3–0.6 per 10,000 per day) (Toole and Waldman 1997), a CMR threshold above 1 per 10,000 per day is considered an emergency situation. The postemergency phase is reached when mortality rates are stabilized below 1 per 10,000 per day and when basic needs have begun to be addressed (Hanquet 1997). The postemergency phase, however, does not mean that the CHE has ended but that the public health emergency, as defined by extremely high mortality and morbidity, has been contained. Public health objectives for this phase, also designated the "care and maintenance" phase by the United Nations

High Commissioner for Refugees (UNHCR) (Zetter 1999), are to consolidate and maintain population health status, prepare for new disease outbreaks and new arrivals of people and begin the process of enhancing program sustainability through "reducing assistance in line with decreased needs, encouraging better use of local resources" (Hanquet 1997:246) and strengthening local capacity and self-sufficiency among the local and refugee population.

Many ongoing CHEs have progressed beyond the immediate crisis to become "chronic"—for example, those of South Sudan, Sierra Leone, Angola, Sri Lanka, and Afghanistan. Responding effectively and appropriately has become more difficult in these complex political and social environments. Interventions are often dangerous, contentious and carry enormous risks for relief workers (see Sheik et al. 2000). Relief agencies working in these situations are also increasingly expected to address concerns for equity, participation, effectiveness, and efficiency with a view to longer-term sustainability in a future, more stable environment (Macrae et al. 1997).

The transition and links between the emergency and postemergency phases are unclear, debated (Hanquet 1997; Zetter 1999), and contested. In relation to public health, certain questions arise regarding whether the highly medicalized, top-down interventions, which are characteristic of the acute phase, are capable of adaptation in the postemergency phase. Should agencies adopt practices and attitudes towards the displaced in the acute phase that facilitate recognition of the longer-term challenges of sustainability and refugee self-sufficiency and ownership? And, if they are to do so, how is it to be achieved? Furthermore, what are the likely consequences of a response in which the beneficiaries appear to be treated as passive bystanders in the stabilisation of their own health and social context?

Because humanitarian assistance is often mobilized at the point of serious crisis for a population, there is common agreement that the initial public health response urgently be directed to saving lives and controlling excessive mortality (Hanquet 1997; Noji and Burkholder 1999; Toole and Waldman 1997). Some commentators have argued that there is a tendency for relief agencies in these situations to effect a universal relief model (Hanquet 1997) and, in the interests of a speedy response, emergency efforts may be established on assumptions of need largely based on previous experience in complex emergencies (Davis 1996; Howarth 1996). In the recent mass exodus of Kosovar Albanians from Kosovo in 1999, the humanitarian community was ready to offer responses developed through years of experience of complex emergencies in Africa, heavily focusing, for example, on the control of communicable diseases. They found, however, that the most pressing problems related to the lack of availability of drugs for continuing to treat chronic disorders in the elderly, and to people's anxiety at not being able to have telephonic communication with other family members.

Médecins Sans Frontières (MSF) points out that, in these situations, the "priority is to meet the most basic human needs, without consideration for the individual social and cultural background of different refugee populations" (Hanquet 1997:23). However, neglect of refugees' perspectives and involvement, even in this phase when attention is directed to saving lives, may have implications for the effectiveness of assistance programs (African Rights 1994; Hanquet 1997; Zetter 1999).

Even within the emergency paradigm, however, there are concerns that recognized good practice could be overlooked in the urgency of an emergency, with potentially serious consequences for the displaced population. For example, diarrheal diseases, particularly dysentery and cholera, commonly cause high rates of mortality and morbidity during CHEs (Noji and Burkholder 1999). In July 1994, the outbreak of overlapping diarrheal epidemics in Goma, Zaire, and surrounding camps resulted in approximately 50,000 deaths; the average CMR for this period reached peaks between 28.1 and 44.9 per 10,000 per day (Goma Epidemiology Group 1995). Public health practice in these situations is to prioritize actions to mitigate the consequences of epidemics in camps, including the organization of chlorination brigades at untreated water sources, the designation of physically isolated defecation fields, community outreach to identify and treat patients outside of clinics, oral rehydration therapy, and emphasis on education about personal hygiene and the provision of soap (Goma Epidemiology Group 1995). Very few of these actions had been undertaken at the time of the outbreak in the Goma area. Subsequent evaluations discovered that approximately 47 percent of those who died of cholera "had never sought health care" largely because of the lack of outreach programs in operation at that stage, the inability of refugees to reach health facilities and inadequate utilization and promotion of oral rehydration therapy by relief workers (Goma Epidemiology Group 1995:341). Noji and Burkholder (1999) compared this with the response to cholera epidemics that occurred later in the Ngara (Tanzania) camps. There, several key actions were prioritized, albeit with sufficient time to put them into place, including "well-developed programs to mobilize the community, with many community health workers and community awareness groups who promoted early case-finding and referral to [dedicated cholera] centers" and a "well-motivated population conscious of what had happened five months earlier in Goma" (Noji and Burkholder 1999:47). These two factors, in particular, highlight the pivotal role that the community plays in responding to its own health needs as part of a wider public health response. The importance of broadening the involvement in public health beyond formal emergency workers cannot be overstated. As Harrison (1996) argues in relation to sanitation, "in the first few days of an emergency, almost the only sanitation tool likely to be available is health education about practices concerning defecation, washing, and water storage and disposal. Community coop-eration is essential, and people may need instruction in the appropriate way to use unfamiliar sanitation facilities" (1996:26).

Not only are participatory techniques necessary to convey informa-tion, but also, perhaps more importantly, they are necessary to collectively identify and support appropriate responses and develop innovative but acceptable interventions in response to key health and social challenges.

Rapid Assessment—What Do We Need to Know?

Besides identifying the needs of the displaced population, rapid needs assessment in the initial phase of a CHE should also ensure that the type of assistance provided is appropriate and targeted toward the most vulnerable groups in the population (Hanquet 1997; Noji and Burkholder 1999; The Sphere Project 1998; Toole 1999).[1] Such recommended good practice represents a step forward in ensuring a broader view of needs and recognition of process, thus contributing to program effectiveness (Howarth 1996; Toole 1999). Yet, the process itself rests on a series of as-sumptions about what is "appropriate" and who is "vulnerable." Who deter-mines the criteria and indicators for these objectives? How will the informa-tion on which priorities will be based be gathered, and from whom? A concern for methodology and process is critical, since this will have a cru-cial impact on the response (Jok 1998; Sommers 1995).

The concept of appropriate health actions during emergencies varies greatly among different relief agencies. There are many critiques of "inap-propriate" actions (Harrell-Bond 1999), but no clear consensus about what constitutes "appropriate" actions beyond saving lives and protecting civil-ians; these objectives in themselves constitute a continuing challenge to most agencies. Weiss and Collins suggest that "all too often . . . the hu-manitarian system considers victims *objects of assistance*. The process of delivering humanitarian assistance has in some instances taken priority over the objective of making civilians self-sustaining as soon as possible" (1996:160). Briggs and Leong raise questions about the relevance and ap-propriateness of secondary—the "restoration of the health status of the af-fected population"—and tertiary—the "promotion of a higher level of health status than that attained prior to the emergency"(1999:79)—objectives in CHEs, which go beyond the primary objective of mitigating mortality and morbidity. However, unlike disaster response in non-CHE settings, in which resources for the ongoing generic health needs of the population are more likely to be met (Briggs and Leong 1999), Sapir (1991) suggests that population health needs in CHEs encompass "all aspects of a normal health structure with some additional specificities" (1991:177) with impli-cations for assessment. In many CHE situations, she argues, the challenge may be one of establishing a relatively comprehensive health program within a significantly reduced time frame. This suggests a substantial role for community involvement in planning and implementing of emergency programs.

As stated earlier, consideration of the role of the community is frequently absent in the *acute* phase of the emergency, while given greater prominence in the *post*emergency phase. Yet the perception of refugees as helpless "victims" in the acute phase repeatedly results in programs that are formulated and implemented from the top down, with the consequence that key cultural and social variables affecting program effectiveness and acceptability are overlooked (Hanquet 1997; Pottier 1996; Slim 1998). In other circumstances, affected populations may inadvertently be blamed for getting themselves into the crisis situation (Weiss and Collins 1996). In primary health care theory, if not in practice, appropriateness is strongly connected to program designs that are culturally sensitive, relevant to local needs and accepted by the community (Brown et al. 1998; Macdonald 1992; World Health Organization/United Nations Children's Fund 1978). Toole (1999) advises, for example, that information about preexisting conditions, such as health beliefs and cultural attitudes to health services, be included in the initial needs assessment during CHEs. While anthropologists agree, they also acknowledge that this is often difficult in the chaos in the early stages of an emergency and may require skills not possessed by emergency public health planners (Jok 1998; Pottier 1996). Busza and Lush (1999) also suggest that much relevant information concerning CHE-affected populations could be collated from preexisting research and analyses. Boelaert et al. (1999), however, worry that a lack of time and capacity to discuss health issues with refugee communities in acute emergencies may "persist long after the initial emergency is over" (1999:175). Prioritizing needs is then left to the perceptions and values of outsiders, despite potentially quite different priorities perceived by the affected population (Palmer 1999; Toole 1999). Such a clash of perceptions is noted, for example, in identifying infants and children under five as the most vulnerable and deserving of relief assistance, which may reflect a set of Northern assumptions and cultural values (Boyden and Gibbs 1997; Davis 1996; Slim 1998). Palmer (1999) notes a similar gap in relation to reproductive health. She found that service providers and male community leaders in southern Sudan gave little credence to reproductive health issues, while women clearly perceived such services to be a priority.

Understanding community health beliefs and care seeking behavior is necessary to design appropriate and acceptable services (Green 1999; Habgood 1998; Jok 1998; McCombie 1999). Very little in-depth research, however, has been published examining the interaction between emergency public health policy, as outlined above, and prevailing health beliefs and cultural attitudes to services. While Harrell-Bond (1986, 1999), in particular, has been a consistent voice in highlighting the refugees' perspective, most research of this kind has been undertaken in relation to the psychosocial consequences of conflict (Boyden and Gibbs 1997; Bracken and Petty 1998; Summerfield 1999) or reproductive health (Palmer and Zwi 1998) rather than the more standard public health concerns. Nor is there little information about host populations and their perspectives on health, health services and issues of access and quality, yet their needs and views too are central to offering appropriate services. More such research relevant to public health issues is needed; existing policies can then be reviewed based on research that seeks to comprehend the lived experience of refugees and the extent to which international relief agencies have understood their needs.

Jok (1998), for example, has undertaken an exceptional study reviewing the perspectives of Dinka women and men in South Sudan, regarding sexual and reproductive health and their experience with international relief. Jok's study, which focused on people internally displaced whose lives and social worlds have been shattered by chronic war and instability, found that "even the most accomplished programs have often ignored the potential of social behaviour and cultural practices in limiting the ability of relief workers to reach their target groups, or even identifying those groups" (Jok 1998:276). Pottier (1996) echoes these findings from his study in the Rwandese camps in Ngara and Goma, deploring the "continued absence of detailed knowledge regarding the social, economic and political conditions that prevail in refugee situations" (1996:404) and the negative impact this has had on providing effective and appropriate services (Pottier 1995). Both anthropologists remark on the resilience and capacities of conflict affected people and the necessity for agencies to understand and work with people's own endeavors to reconstruct their societies. Summerfield (1998) asserts that to be relevant, interventions need to be directed to the devastated social world of survivor populations, which embody both the resilience and capacity of survivors "to manage their suffering, adapt and recover on a collective basis" (1998:34).

Yet understanding and engaging with the "social world" of conflict affected populations is fraught with obstacles and difficulties. Personal and group insecurity prevailing in conflict situations makes it difficult to build bridges of trust and cooperation (Jok 1996; Lindenberg 1999; Matlou 1999). An even greater chasm in relationships may result from the very different social and cultural worlds of conflict affected and expatriate humanitarian aid workers. Relief postings are usually short-term, with an operational and technical focus allowing little time for postholders to get to know a war affected community or vice versa. Inexperienced expatriate personnel may feel under pressure to demonstrate their skills by taking on more than necessary (Weiss and Collins 1996). Rapid assessments and monitoring strategies may lead to fixed assumptions that are difficult to shift about community beliefs and social relations (Jok 1998; Marshall 1995; Palmer 1999), reflecting a tendency to view displaced populations as "homogenous" and "undifferentiated," a common criticism of humanitarian programs (Harrell-Bond 1999; Jok 1998). The preferred starting points must be acknowledging the heterogeneity of conflict affected populations and the diversity of groups, subgroups and communities within them; and their resourcefulness and agency in making decisions that affect their lives. Doing so, however, requires policies and strategies to encourage and support approaches to working *with* and involving the refugee population, rather than working *for* them. Given the complexity and range of actors in the humanitarian field, this will represent a significant challenge not only in formulating policies but also in seeing them effectively implemented in the field.

Engendering Emergency Public Health

Gender, a key social and cultural variable, is central to understanding the heterogeneity and diversity in a population, and to appreciating that women and men are affected differently by CHEs and require responses that strategically meet these differences. As Enarson succinctly explains:

> Gendered vulnerability does not derive from a single factor, such as household headship or poverty, but reflects historically and culturally specific patterns of relations in social institutions, culture and personal lives. Intersecting with economic, racial and other inequalities, these relationships create hazardous social conditions placing different groups of women at risk when disastrous events unfold. [1998:159]

Despite the development of international policies that support the integration of gender concerns with emergency responses by different agencies (Eade and Williams 1995; Marshall 1995; Palmer et al. 1999; Walker 1996), the degree to which gender is considered a critical factor in planning and implementing emergency programs is still contested (Boelaert et. al 1999; Enarson 1998; Giles 1999; Marshall 1995; Palmer and Zwi 1998). From the onset of the emergency response, health data collected through needs assessments and public health surveillance is often not disaggregated by sex (Palmer and Zwi 1998; Toole 1993), an oversight that fails to acknowledge gender-specific vulnerability and may hide it when it exists. In a Somali refugee camp in Kenya, for example, Boelaert et al. (1999) found that no gender-specific morbidity data were routinely collected, apart from hospital admission data. If no effort is taken to record potential variations in health problems or use of services by sex, age, ethnicity, social class, or other variables, then differentials in distribution of support or access to services that reflect these dimensions will not be revealed and will not be identified as a problem deserving a response.

Assessment methods that seek qualitative information also frequently fall short of collecting gender-sensitive data. In most refugee situations, educated refugees routinely become the "gatekeepers" to the community, acting as "key informants" or community representatives. In many societies, men dominate this role as they are more likely to be educated, publicly articulate and, most importantly, able to speak a European language

(Hanquet 1997; Jok 1998; Matlou 1999). Sommers, for example, observed the "almost complete dominance of educated men over refugee discourse" (1995:19) in relation to Burundi refugees in Tanzania, in part due to their ability to speak French and English with UNHCR and government officials, compared with only a small percentage of women who could speak either language. The implication of this often pragmatic response, however, is that the perspectives and needs of women as well as other vulnerable groups are overlooked (Marshall 1995; Matlou 1999; Palmer and Zwi 1998). A commitment to developing inclusive strategies becomes essential if concerns for equity and local ownership are to be met.

Jok (1998) and Palmer (1999) have both observed unwillingness on the part of emergency public health practitioners to respond proactively to the sexual and reproductive health needs of women. Despite sustained efforts at an international level to raise awareness about refugee women's specific health needs (Palmer et al. 1999), at field level reproductive health is considered a "postemergency" issue, not an issue of survival. Therefore, reproductive health is not a priority early in a CHE (Hanquet 1997; Palmer et al. 1999). As Jok argues, the dominance given to communicable disease control in CHEs "often blurs other important aspects of health, and women undergo the silent emergency of reproductive and sexual health problems" (1998:264). Even at the postemergency stage, an unwillingness by emergency workers to engage with the perceived cultural sensitivities related to sexual and reproductive health issues often generates a reluctance to act in accordance with international policy guidelines (Jok 1998; Palmer et al. 1999).

However, when Palmer (1999) asked women in South Sudan about their priorities, they ranked reproductive health much more highly than did either the men or health service providers interviewed. The latter groups apparently had little awareness about the reproductive hazards faced by women. When asked about maternal mortality, men responded that it was not that great and service providers interviewed thought that "not many women die in childbirth," while displaced women in a group discussion presented a more worrying picture: "Many women die in childbirth. Seven to eight last year. Also there are cases of the child dying inside the mother. This problem was there before but has now increased" (Palmer 1999:746). A similar disparity of views prevailed about the extent of abortion and gender-based violence in the community. Service providers felt the abortion issue was not particularly significant, whereas the experiences of community members contradicted this: "Some people don't want to be pregnant, they take herbs and chloroquine injections by breaking the glass and drinking it. They also take Omo [a washing powder] . . . people die because of this" (community leader) and, "Sometimes girls use batteries—99 percent of the girls who do this will die. They pound the batteries, and then they put it in water and drink" (Palmer 1999:745). With respect to gender-based violence, a service provider reported: "Violence against women is not occurring in southern Sudan as women are treasured," whereas an internally displaced woman commented that "no stranger has been violent to me, but at home this violence is normal" (Palmer 1996:746).

As Jok suggests, "women's health needs are not elicited because the right questions are not addressed to the right persons all the needs assessment projects focus on key informants who are usually males of high status" (1998:288). He also argues that

> the way women's reproductive strategies, roles, options and decisions are negotiated at the levels of household, community, state, medical institutions and international health relief, is negatively influenced by women's status which has been further eroded by the war and the "breakdown" of sociocultural institutions among the Dinka of South Sudan. [1998:288]

Even when recognized as an integral part of emergency public health programs, women's health needs are frequently limited to their "biologically determined" reproductive role and, more specifically, pregnancy and childbirth (Boelaert et al. 1999; Jok 1998). There is little recognition of the social and cultural context of women's lives, and how their status as women will, on the one hand, potentially increase their exposure to a range of public health hazards while, on the other hand, limit their access to health services and other resources (Palmer and Zwi 1998). Among Somali refugees in Kenya, Boelaert's team observed, for example, that case detection of tuberculosis resulted in an enrollment of only 20 percent of infected women into a treatment program. On further investigation, it was found that Somali women with tuberculosis faced much greater social stigmatization than men, with their chances of marriage diminished, or even facing expulsion from their families (Boelaert et al. 1999), hence their unwillingness to come forward for treatment. Such sociocultural obstacles, recognized in nonconflict contexts (Hudelson 1999; Rathgeber and Vlassoff 1993), need to be better understood by emergency practitioners and reflected in operational policy guidelines. There is even less recognition of any sense of agency and capability in the hands of affected women.

Although gender related research in relation to conflict is growing and feeding into the development of gender-sensitive policy, other vulnerable groups also continue to be overlooked. Older people, for example, are often considered to have needs that are no different from others, or are assumed to be low priority simply because of their age. Older people, who may make up a considerable proportion of conflict affected populations, especially those in more developed regions such as Kosovo or Chechnya, may have additional problems that result from poorer mobility, increased levels of disability, high levels of psychological distress and functional deterioration, and problems resulting from chronic diseases and the failure or withdrawal of treatment, given the CHE. The particular role of older people in conflict affected communities may easily be overlooked, whereas they may have a powerful role to play in assisting the community to come together, to build upon prior experiences and to look to the future (Zwi 1999). In other situations, older people may be the ones who strongly influence, sometimes negatively, the views of the young by highlighting prior negative experiences of relationships with other groups. Whether their role is positive or negative in rebuilding a sense of community, they are an important group to understand and with whom to interact.

Sustainability and Instability

Although there is a limit to the resources available to provide new services, a reorientation to strategic programming that responds to the diversity of needs and builds on the resources and capacity within the refugee population is urgently needed (Anderson and Woodrow 1998; Lindenberg 1999; Roche 1996). Kibreab suggests that uncertainty in planning in the midst of unstable settings, exacerbated by limited or unreliable data, can be reduced by "tapping into the knowledge and experience of project or programme beneficiaries, and partly by enlisting their support and ensuring their participation in need identification, design, implementation, monitoring and evaluation" (1999:135–136). Such an approach is, of course, not new and represents a developmental perspective to working in CHEs (Commins 1996; Roche 1996). Despite significant debate about the potential pitfalls of working developmentally in CHEs (Macrae et al. 1997), a concern for sustainability, local ownership and relevance demands that all options be explored. Even in the complex political environment of the Rwandese camps in Tanzania, self help initiatives of community groups were supported partly as a means of "promoting the refugees' own search for new, responsible leaders" (Pottier 1996:416). In other settings, local groups generated appropriate responses such as the establishment of soup kitchens in Somalia (African Rights 1994), which helped avoid amassing large amounts of grain and other supplies that inadvertently became a resource over which conflict continued.

Searching for opportunities for refugees and displaced people to articulate their views represents an additional objective of many agencies to reduce conflict and promote peace through programmatic action (Anderson 1999; Lindenberg 1999). Pottier (1996), however, warns against a too uncritical view of refugee society, and argues that refugee nongovernmental organizations (NGO) or "civil society" must be "understood in context and analysed critically" and "not programmatically as an agenda for change," referring in particular to the difficulty of assuring in complex political settings the legitimacy of community leaders and representatives. Bakewell (2000) recognizes that skepticism about the "mantra" of community participation in emergencies is healthy, but nevertheless argues that,

> however top-down, externally driven or otherwise non-participatory an emergency program may be, the benefits or services will not be received passively by the targeted community. They exert agency to mould what is on offer to

their particular interests and incorporate it within their coping strategies. An evaluation of outcomes which uncovers the perspectives of local people may have more chance of understanding the impact of humanitarian assistance and highlight ways that interventions can be built on these local strategies rather than ignore them. [2000:115]

Documenting the practices currently employed by sensitive humanitarian agencies would be a valuable starting point in deriving good practice and promoting learning across organizations. Edwards and Hulme (1995) argue that for many NGOs, "downward accountability" to communities is typically far weaker than "upward accountability" to donors. In discussing development work, they argue that increasing the involvement of grassroots constituencies, including beneficiaries of program activities, is the only way to correct weaknesses in downward accountability. Working in CHEs has its own imperatives, but keeping an eye open to possibilities, potentials, and processes for facilitating improved linkages with affected populations and the communities and subgroups within them, demands our attention if improvements are to be made. Placing agency back in the hands of those affected is a key challenge for humanitarian workers. Smillie comments that, "development is, or should be, a knowledge-based endeavour. The importance of learning what works, and why, is essential to success. Knowing what does not work is almost more important" (1995:158).

Conclusion

The dominant approach in emergency public health has often not considered the significance of context in CHEs, as represented by a diversity of needs and the complexity and turbulence of conflict affected environments. Assessing population health needs has routinely overlooked the degree to which communities, universally, rely on social networks and cultural institutions for support in negotiating their daily health needs, broadly defined. Alongside physical destruction and devastation, the social and cultural environments integral to societal well-being have been eroded and/or targeted by opposing sides in conflict. What replaces these sociocultural institutions is often contested and unclear in their ability to meet the needs of the community, particularly those of vulnerable groups. In South Sudan, Jok (1998) has described, for example, how "newly emergent Dinka social and cultural institutions" have further disempowered women resulting in a worsened situation for their sexual and reproductive health. He also describes the inability of international relief agencies to understand how this changing social, economic, and political environment has had consequences for health.

Illsley and Mullen (1991) describe research needs in relation to disadvantaged client groups in general health services. They identify four important gaps, which can be adapted to highlight needs in CHEs. They argue for the need to (1) produce data, on a routine basis, relating to the health status of disadvantaged groups; (2) develop more sensitive and accurate indicators of health, disease, sickness, and functioning; (3) develop knowledge of the natural history of the health consequences of disadvantage; and (4) accumulate knowledge about the use of health services by disadvantaged groups. Even in the best of circumstances and with services with the greatest resources, such analyses represent a major challenge; responding holistically is even more difficult in CHE settings. The analyses are necessarily based within community perspectives and their interfaces with service provision, and seek not only to identify the typical experience but the range of extreme and varied experiences that contribute to a perception of what is "typical." Using such data to strengthen and build on the capabilities and agency of those affected deserves attention.

Development of good practice methods for rapid assessment of the composition and differential interests of groups and subgroups within conflict affected populations would be valuable. More sensitive analyses will not only build upon earlier ethnographic, anthropologic, sociological, and public health analyses of the particular populations affected by conflict, but will reflect a different and more appropriate perspective. It remains a key challenge to draw upon such information to derive insights helping to ensure that context appropriate services can be provided and that prosocial capital (Goodhand and Hulme 1999) can be rebuilt within affected communities. Bakewell states emphatically that "neglecting the life and world of local people will make it impossible to understand the process by which external interventions are mediated at the local level to give particular outcomes, and valuable lessons which help alleviate suffering will be lost" (2000:103).

Although policy that recognizes the heterogeneity of displaced populations exists, it is unclear to what extent these concerns have impacted emergency public health practice. Finding the appropriate balance between delivering services and being responsive to community perceptions, perspectives, needs, demands, desires, capacity, and agency is a key challenge. That one should develop an appropriate balance by correcting the present imbalance is clear; precisely how to do so is not.

Note

1. See Chapter 1 for further description of rapid assessment.

References Cited

African Rights
    1994   Humanitarianism Unbound: Current Dilemmas Facing Multi-Mandate Relief Operations in Political Emergencies. Discussion Paper no. 5. London: African Rights.
Aglionby, J., and C. Zinn
    1999   City's Destruction Now Complete. The Guardian, September 9. Electronic document, http://www.newsUnlimited.ues.org/Geopolitics/EastTimor.asp.

Anderson, Mary
    1999   Do No Harm: How Aid Can Support Peace—or War. Boulder: Lynne Reinner Pub-
    lishers.
Anderson, Mary B., and Peter Woodrow
    1998   Rising from the Ashes: Development Strategies in Times of Disaster. London: IT
    Publications.
Bakewell, Oliver
    2000   Uncovering Local Perspectives on Humanitarian Assistance and Its Outcomes.
    Disasters 24:103–116.
Banatvala, Nicholas, Bruce Laurence, and Timothy Healing
    1999   Paediatric Care in Disaster and Refugee Settings. In Recent Advances in Peadia-
    trics. T. J. David, ed. Edinburgh: Livingstone Publishers.
Baum, Francis
    1995   Researching Public Health: Behind the Qualitative-Quantitative Methodological
    Debate. Social Science and Medicine 40:459–468.
Boelaert, Marleen, Fabienne Vautier, Tine Dusauchoit, Wim Van Damme, and
Monique Van Dormael
    1999   The Relevance of Gendered Approaches to Refugee Health: A Case Study in Ha-
    gadera, Kenya. In Engendering Forced Migration: Theory and Practice. Doreen Indra,
    ed. Pp. 165–176. New York: Berghahn Books.
Bok, Sissela
    1999   The New Ethical Boundaries. In Humanitarian Crises: The Medical and Public
    Health Response. Jennifer Leaning, Susan M. Briggs, and Lincoln C. Chen, eds. Pp.
    179–193. Cambridge, MA: Harvard University Press.
Boyden, Jo, and Sara Gibbs
    1997   Children of War: Responses to Psycho-Social Distress in Cambodia. Geneva:
    United Nations Research Institute for Social Development.
Bracken, Patrick J., and Celia Petty
    1998   Rethinking the Trauma of War. London: Free Association Books.
Briggs, Susan, and Mark Leong
    1999   Classic Concepts in Disaster Medical Response. In Humanitarian Crises: The
    Medical and Public Health Response. Jennifer Leaning, Susan M. Briggs, and Lincoln
    C. Chen, eds. Pp. 69–79. Cambridge, MA: Harvard University Press.
Brown, Peter J., Ronald J. Barrett, and Mark B. Padilla
    1998   Medical Anthropology: An Introduction to the Field. In Understanding and Apply-
    ing Medical Anthropology. Peter J. Brown, ed. Pp. 10–19. Mountain View, CA: Mayfield
    Publishing Company.
Busza, Joanna, and Louisiana Lush
    1999   Planning Reproductive Health in Conflict: A Conceptual Framework. Social Sci-
    ence and Medicine 49:155–171.
Cliffe, Lionel, and Robin Luckham
    1999   Complex Political Emergencies and the State: Failure and the Fate of the State.
    Third World Quarterly 20:27–50.
Commins, Stephen
    1996   In the Line of Fire: Development in Conflict. In Development in States of War: Se-
    lected Articles from Development in Practice. Deborah Eade, ed. Pp. 8–14. Oxford: Ox-
    fam Publications.
Davis, Austen
    1996   Targeting the Vulnerable in Emergency Situations: Who Is Vulnerable? Lancet 348:
    868–871.
Duffield, Mark
    1994a   Complex Emergencies and the Crisis of Developmentalism. IDS Bulletin 25(4):
    37–45.
    1994b   The Political Economy of Internal War: Asset Transfer, Complex Emergencies and
    International Aid. In War and Hunger: Rethinking International Responses to Complex
    Emergencies. Joanna Macrae and Anthony Zwi, eds. Pp. 50–69. London: Zed Press.
Eade, Deborah, and Suzanne Williams
    1995   The Oxfam Handbook of Development and Relief, vol. 2. Oxford: Oxfam Publica-
    tions.

Edwards, Michael, and David Hulme
  1995 Beyond the Magic Bullet? Lessons and Conclusions. *In* Non-Governmental Organ-
    isations: Performance and Accountability. Beyond the Magic Bullet. Michael Edwards
    and David Hulme, eds. Pp. 219–228. London: Earthscan.
Enarson, Elaine
  1998 Through Women's Eyes: A Gendered Research Agenda for Disaster Social Sci-
    ence. Disasters 22:157–173.
Giles, Wenona
  1999 Gendered Violence in War: Reflections on Transnationalist and Comparative
    Frameworks in Militarized Conflict Zones. *In* Engendering Forced Migration: Theory and
    Practice. Doreen Indra, ed. Pp. 83–93. New York: Berghahn Books.
Goma Epidemiology Group
  1995 Public Health Impact of Rwanda Refugee Crisis: What Happened in Goma, Zaire,
    in July 1994? Lancet 345:339–343.
Goodhand, Jonathan, and David Hulme
  1999 From Wars to Complex Political Emergencies: Understanding Conflict and Peace-
    Building in the New World Disorder. Third World Quarterly 20:13–26.
Green, Andrew
  1999 An Introduction to Health Planning in Developing Countries. (Second ed.). Oxford:
    Oxford University Press.
Habgood, Laura
  1998 Health and Livelihoods in Rural Angola: A Participatory Research Project. Oxford:
    Oxfam Publications.
Hanquet, Germaine, ed.
  1997 Refugee Health: An Approach to Emergency Situations. London: Macmillan Edu-
    cation Ltd.
Harrell-Bond, Barbara
  1986 Imposing Aid: Emergency Assistance to Refugees. Oxford: Oxford University
    Press.
  1999 The Experience of Refugees as Recipients of Aid. *In* Refugees: Perspectives on
    the Experience of Forced Migration. Alastair Ager, ed. Pp. 136–168. London: Cassell.
Harrison, Bryony
  1996 Sanitation in Emergency Situations. Africa Health 18:26.
Howarth, John
  1996 A Minimum Data Set for Emergencies. Africa Health 18:18–20.
Hudelson, Patricia
  1999 Gender Issues in the Detection and Treatment of Tuberculosis. *In* Tuberculosis: An
    Interdisciplinary Perspective. J. D. H. Porter and J. M. Grange, eds. Pp. 339–355. Lon-
    don: Imperial College Press.
Illsley, Raymond, and Kenneth Mullen
  1991 The Health Needs of Disadvantaged Client Groups. *In* Oxford Textbook of Public
    Health. W. W. Holland, R. Detels, and G. Knox, eds. Pp. 539–554. Oxford: Oxford Uni-
    versity Press.
Jean, Francois
  1995 Rwanda. *In* Populations in Danger. Francois Jean, ed. Pp. 32–46. Paris: La Decou-
    verte/Médicins Sans Frontières.
Jok, Madut Jok
  1998 Militarization, Gender and Reproductive Health in South Sudan. New York: Edwin
    Mellen Press.
  1996 Information Exchange in the Disaster Zone: Interaction Between Aid Workers and
    Recipients in South Sudan. Disasters 20:206–215.
Jones, Linda
  1994 The Social Context of Health and Health Work. London: Macmillan.
Kaldor, Mary
  1993 Yugoslavia and the New Nationalism. New Left Review 197:96–112.
Kibreab, Gaim
  1999 The Consequences of Non-Participatory Planning: Lessons from a Livestock Provi-
    sion Project to Returnees in Eritrea. Journal of Refugee Studies 12:135–160.

Leaning, Jennifer
  1999 Introduction. *In* Humanitarian Crises: The Medical and Public Health Response.
    Jennifer Leaning, Susan M. Briggs, and Lincoln C. Chen, eds. Pp. 1–11. Cambridge,
    MA: Harvard University Press.
Lee, P., and D. Paxman
  1997 Reinventing Public Health. Annual Review of Public Health 18:1–35.
Levine, Ian
  1997 Promoting Humanitarian Principles: The Southern Sudan Experience. Relief and
    Rehabilitation Network Paper, No. 21. London: Overseas Development Institute.
Lindenberg, Marc
  1999 Complex Emergencies and NGOs. *In* Humanitarian Crises: The Medical and Pub-
    lic Health Response. Jennifer Leaning, Susan M. Briggs, and Lincoln C. Chen, eds. Pp.
    211–245. Cambridge, MA: Harvard University Press.
Macdonald, John
  1992 Primary Health Care. Medicine in Its Place. London: Earthscan Publications.
Macrae, Joanna, Mark Bradbury, Susanne Jaspars, D. Johnson, and Mark Duffield
  1997 Conflict, the Continuum and Chronic Emergencies: A Critical Analysis of the Scope
    for Linking Relief, Rehabilitation and Development Planning in Sudan. Disasters
    21:223–243.
Marshall, R.
  1995 "Refugees, Feminine Plural" Refugees: Refugee Women, No. 100. Electronic docu-
    ment, http://www.unhcr.ch/pubs/rm100/rm10001.htm.
Matlou, Patrick
  1999 Upsetting the Cart: Forced Migration and Gender Issues, the African Experience.
    In Engendering Forced Migration: Theory and Practice. Doreen Indra, ed. Pp. 128–145.
    New York: Berghahn Books.
McCombie, Susan
  1999 Folk Flu and Viral Syndrome: An Anthropological Perspective. *In* Anthropology in
    Public Health: Bridging Differences in Culture and Society. Robert Hahn, ed. Pp. 27–43.
    New York: Oxford University Press.
Noji, Eric, and Brent Burkholder
  1999 Public Health Interventions. *In* Humanitarian Crises: The Medical and Public Health
    Response. Jennifer Leaning, Susan M. Briggs, and Lincoln C. Chen, eds. Pp. 41–67.
    Cambridge, MA: Harvard University Press.
Palmer, Celia
  1999 Rapid Appraisal of Needs in Reproductive Health Care in Southern Sudan: Qualita-
    tive Study. British Medical Journal 319:743–748.
Palmer, Celia, Louisiana Lush, and Anthony Zwi
  1999 The Emerging International Policy Agenda for Reproductive Health Services in
    Conflict Settings. Social Science and Medicine 49:1689–1703.
Palmer, Celia, and Anthony Zwi
  1998 Women, Health and Humanitarian Aid in Conflict. Disasters 22:236–249.
Pottier, Johan
  1995 Why Aid Agencies Need Better Understanding of the Communities They Assist:
    The Experience of Food Aid in Rwandan Refugee Camps. Disasters 20:324–337.
  1996 Relief and Repatriation: Views by Rwandan Refugees. Lessons for Humanitarian
    Aid Workers. African Affairs 5:403–429.
Rathgeber, E., and Carol Vlassof
  1993 Gender and Tropical Diseases: A New Research Focus. Social Science and Medi-
    cine 37:513–520.
Reed, Holly, John Haaga, and Charles Keely, eds.
  1998 The Demography of Forced Migration: Summary of a Workshop. Committee on
    Population, Commission on Behavioral and Social Sciences and Education, National
    Research Council. Washington, DC: National Academy Press.
Roche, Chris
  1996 Operationality in Turbulence: The Need for Change. *In* Development in States of
    War; Selected Articles from Development in Practice. Deborah Eade, ed. Pp. 15–25.
    Oxford: Oxfam Publications.

Sapir, Debarati Guha
     1991   Rapid Assessment of Health Needs in Mass Emergencies: Review of Current Con-
        cepts and Methods. World Health Statistical Quarterly 44:171–181.
Schmeidl, Suzanne
     1998   Comparative Trends in Forced Displacement: IDPs and Refugees, 1964–96. In In-
        ternally Displaced People: A Global Survey. Janie Hampton, ed. Pp. 24–33. London:
        Earthscan Publications/Global IDP Survey and Norwegian Refugee Council.
Sheik, Mani, Maria Isabel Gutierrez, Paul Bolton, Paul Spiegel, Michel Thieren, and
Gilbert Burnham
     2000   Deaths among Humanitarian Workers. British Medical Journal 321:166–168.
Slim, Hugo
     1998   Relief Agencies: Cultural Challenges and Cultural Responsibility. Report of a Semi-
        nar for Non-Governmental Organizations on Humanitarian Standards and Cultural Dif-
        ferences, Geneva: International Committee of the Red Cross and the Geneva
        Foundation, December 14.
Smillie, Ian
     1995   Painting Canadian Roses Red. In Non-Governmental Organisations: Performance
        and Accountability. Beyond the Magic Bullet. M. Edwards and D. Hulme, eds. Pp.
        157–166. London: Earthscan.
Sommers, Marc
     1995   Representing Refugees: The Role of Elites in Burundi Refugee Society. Disasters
        19:19–25.
The Sphere Project
     1998   Humanitarian Charter and Minimum Standards in Disaster Response. Geneva:
        Steering Committee for Humanitarian Response and Interaction.
Summerfield, Derek
     1998   The Social Experience of War and Some Issues for the Humanitarian Field. In Re-
        thinking the Trauma of War. Patrick J. Bracken and Celia Petty, eds. Pp. 9–37. London:
        Free Association Books.
     1999   Sociocultural Dimensions of War, Conflict, and Displacement. In Refugees: Per-
        spectives on the Experience of Forced Migration. Alastair Ager, ed. Pp. 111–135. Lon-
        don: Cassell.
Toole, Michael
     1993   The Public Health Consequences of Inaction: Lessons Learned in Responding to
        Sudden Population Displacements. In A Framework for Survival: Health, Human Rights
        and Humanitarian Assistance in Conflicts and Disasters. Kevin M. Cahill, ed. Pp.
        144–158. Washington, DC: Council on Foreign Relations.
     1999   The Role of Rapid Assessment. In Humanitarian Crises: The Medical and Public
        Health Response. Jennifer Leaning, Susan M. Briggs, and Lincoln C. Chen, eds. Pp.
        15–39. Cambridge, MA: Harvard University Press.
Toole, Michael, and Ronald Waldman
     1997   The Public Health Aspects of Complex Emergencies and Refugee Situations. An-
        nual Review of Public Health 18:283–312.
Walker, Bridget
     1996   Overcoming the Tyranny of the Urgent. Development and Gender in Brief 4:1–2.
Weiss, Thomas G., and Cindy Collins
     1996   Humanitarian Challenges and Intervention. World Politics and The Dilemmas of
        Help. Boulder: Westview Press.
World Health Organization
     1999   Rapid Health Assessment Protocols for Emergencies. Geneva: World Health Or-
        ganization.
World Health Organization/United Nations Children's Fund
     1978   Primary Health Care: A Joint Report. International Conference on Primary Health
        Care, Alma Ata, USSR. Geneva, World Health Organization, September 6–12.
Zetter, Roger
     1999   International Perspectives on Refugee Experience. In Refugees: Perspectives on
        the Experience of Forced Migration. Alastair Ager, ed. Pp. 46–82. London: Cassell.

Zwi, Anthony
    1996   Numbering the Dead: Counting the Casualties of War. *In* Defining Violence: Under-
        standing the Causes and Effects of Violence. Hannah Bradby, ed. Pp. 99–124. Alder-
        shot: Avebury Press.
    1999   Conflict, Humanitarian Assistance and Older People. *In* The Ageing and Develop-
        ment Report: Poverty, Independence and the World's Older People. J. Randel, T. Ger-
        man, and D. Ewing, eds. Pp. 108–117. London: Earthscan.
Zwi, Anthony, Suzanne Fustukian, and Dinesh Sethi
    1999   Never Again, Once Again. Learning Public Health Lessons from the Kosovo Crisis.
        European Journal of Public Health 9:81–82.

CHAPTER 3

Human Rights and Complex Emergencies

Lucia Ann McSpadden
Life and Peace Institute

John R. MacArthur
Malaria Epidemiology Branch, Division of Parasitic Diseases, National Center for Infectious Diseases, Centers for Disease Control and Prevention

> Within a system which denies the existence of basic human rights, fear tends to be the order of the day. Fear of imprisonment, fear of torture, fear of death, fear of losing friends, family, property or means of livelihood, fear of poverty, fear of isolation, fear of failure.
>
> —Aung San Suu Kyi, Nobel Peace Prize Winner, *Freedom from Fear* (1991:184)

Human rights abuses are embedded within complex humanitarian emergencies (CHE). The terse term *complex emergencies* describes local, regional, national, and international systems overwhelmed by the rapid, large-scale movement of people fleeing actual or anticipated human rights abuses.

Recent figures from the U.S. Committee on Refugees state that there are more than 35 million persons uprooted worldwide—an increase of five million over 1998 (U.S. Committee for Refugees 2000).[1] As the United Nations High Commissioner for Refugees (UNHCR) stresses, "violations of human rights are a major—indeed, the major—cause of mass population displacement" (UNHCR:58) in spite of politicians', media's, governments', and even nongovernmental organizations' (NGO) assertions to the contrary (UNHCR 1995b).

The origins of population displacement have changed since the fall of the former Soviet Union. In the past, persons fled because of political ideological differences, individual acts of persecution, and/or to escape proxy wars being fought by global superpowers in developing countries. During the last decade, we have seen flight stem from a different set of circumstances: intrastate conflicts, often fueled by ethnic or religious antagonisms, weakened states because of poverty and economic collapse and ecological disasters.[2]

Torture and other abuses have a direct (and indirect) link to mass population displacement. People leave their homes in attempt to seek protection from widespread violence originating from either intentional targeting or getting caught between warring groups. Yet, in spite of international agreements, over 93 countries still practice torture (Basoglu 1993).

Human rights, within complex emergencies during the initial phases of humanitarian relief, are the focus of our discussion. Our concern is with the planning and implementation of the response system, especially as it affects health and well being. Our intent is to provide anthropologists and other social scientists, especially those with medical expertise engaged in these efforts, with brief descriptions and analyses of selected human rights concerns within complex emergencies. We offer some suggestions for protecting the human rights of the persons we intend to help.[3]

Background

The protection of human rights has been prominent on the international agenda since World War II, and was a founding principle in the establishment of the United Nations (UN) in 1945. The standards for human rights were codified in the Universal Declaration of Human Rights, the International Covenant of Civil and Political Rights, and the International Covenant on Economic, Social and Cultural Rights (Mann et al. 1994). A number of other UN conventions have built upon this foundation in the ensuing years, covering such areas as discrimination, child rights and torture.[4] With the establishment of the office of the UN High Commissioner for Human Rights in December 1993, global attention towards human rights has been intensified.

According to the United Nation's *Universal Declaration of Human Rights,* "all human beings . . . without distinction of any kind" (1948:6–9) have a right to life, liberty, and security of person. They have the right not to be subjected to torture, slavery, or arbitrary detention or exile. They have the right to own property, to move freely within the borders of their country, and to be protected against arbitrary interference into their personal and family life. One's honor and reputation are not to be attacked. The family is recognized as the fundamental social group and thus entitled to protection as a human right (United Nations 1948).

Although the protection of human rights was the foundation of the 1951 UN Convention and the 1967 Protocol Relating to the Status of Refugees, as well as the primary responsibility of the Office of the UN High Commissioner for Refugees (McSpadden and Chol 1998), few relief workers understand the international laws enacted to protect refugees. Furthermore, even with an understanding of the laws, aid organizations have not developed clear policies for their personnel when they become aware of human rights violations (Waldman and Martone 1999).

With violence propelling people to flee, humanitarian relief organizations have a growing awareness of the need to be more sensitive to human rights violations within the populations being served. As civilians are increasingly the targets of such abuses, the health consequences—both physical and psychological—are more of a concern for public health workers (Waldman and Martone 1999). These consequences are obvious; for example, people who survive torture have health problems (Mann et al. 1994). What are less evident or given less attention are possible human rights abuses within international and local responses to these complex emergencies.

CHEs require the rapid response of the local and international communities. Since the morbidity and mortality rates within the displaced population are very high during the acute phase of the emergency, emphasis is placed on public health interventions. The three central functions of public health include: assessing needs and problems, developing strategies to address areas of priority, and implementing public health programs aimed at combating these problems (Institute of Medicine 1988). When a relief team conducts public health programs comprising each of these areas, there may be possible infringements if a human rights perspective is not used (Mann et al. 1994).

For example, programs in mental health and reproductive health are among the most neglected (Dick and Simmonds 1983; Waldman and Martone 1999), thus restricting the displaced population's right to health. Other rights are just not recognized in spite of rhetoric about the right to live in safety and dignity.

Our discussion is organized around the following topics, chosen because they are factors of dominance, inequity and/or marginalization affecting health, well-being, and treatment of diseases: power imbalances, protection, access to resources, rights of the host communities, gender, and the roles of the anthropologist. In addition, as torture may be a prominent feature of the complex emergency, and because of the need for certain skills to address displaced populations, we also discuss the issue of interviewing torture survivors.[5] There is overlap in these topics; it is for convenience and focus that we separate them. These are also factors that anthropologists may well have the expertise to investigate and analyze.

Power Imbalances

Human rights abuses typically originate from pervasive and systemic power imbalances within the socioeconomic/political/cultural system. These power imbalances most often are embedded within the social structures of the society. When we speak of vulnerable groups such as young children, elderly, women, physically disabled, people with chronic or acute illnesses, or mentally disabled or unaccompanied minors, we are speaking of power imbalances. These persons are vulnerable because they cannot exert the same level of authority, influence, or access as other groups within their social system. They are dependent socially and economically, and this dependency is only enhanced by the effects of displacement in a complex emergency.

At first glance, speaking of such vulnerable groups in medical or health terms is obvious; there are specific needs that need attention and response. Adequate food for malnourished children is essential. People with malaria should be treated and, where possible, the spread of malarial transmission halted or diminished. Pregnant women need specialized care. Infant diarrhea must be prevented or treated rapidly. However, these medical needs also place persons in a less powerful position within their own society; others must look out for and care for them. This social dependency is especially problematic when the entire group of refugees is experiencing limited resources, fear and anxiety, concern for survival, depression, and sorrow because of severe loss.

Looking at these vulnerable groups with a human rights perspective, and examining the effect of power differentials, one needs to ask questions such as:

- What are their particular needs that must be met through social and cultural systems; e.g., who brings them water if they are not able to stand in line for hours?
- How are their special needs raised to the attention of the agency personnel; e.g., who are their spokespersons?
- What is the social system of response to their needs; e.g., who will protect them when resources are limited or access to resources is complex and/or difficult?
- Does group identity affect how the social system operates? Does one clan work to ensure that their members get the resources they need and want before members of the other clans?
- What about social status? Who are those with higher status and what social benefits are understood to be their "right"? For example, are landowners and tenant farmers here together? If so, are the tenant farmers expected to defer to the landowners and, if they are, how does that happen within the relief system and within refugee camps or other displacement settlements?
- What about educational differentials? Are the better educated speaking for the illiterate and, if so, with what level of knowledge and sensitivity?
- What about the women, social status issues, and access to resources or protection?
- What are the internal power dynamics within the household, especially those that affect the distribution and consumption of food?

- When a woman loses her spouse, what are the social consequences for her within the emergency context?
- Who cares for unaccompanied minors, and how are their particular needs addressed within the context of the society?
- Does anyone notice these power differentials?
- Does anyone question them and the consequences of the imbalances?

In the stifling heat of Thika refugee camp housing Ethiopian and Somali refugees, 25 kilometers outside of Nairobi, there is not one tree in sight. The sun beats down. The only shade is within small huts or next to a wall. The elevation is such that malaria is not endemic; most of the highland Ethiopian refugees are unaffected. This is small comfort for the Somali woman lying outside on a sheet, shaking with malarial fevers. No one speaks to her; no one sits with her. It is mid-day and others are busy lining up for water. Where is her social support system? [McSpadden 1992]

A common power imbalance experience is to have those men in higher status social positions become the spokespersons for men and women of lesser status.

These "patrons" become the resource brokers, interpreting to health and aid workers the social and health situation, the needs and suggested ways of response. Most often the responses suggested and the role of spokesperson itself enhance the power differentials of that spokesperson within his community. If the spokesperson represents a particular segment of the community, it is not surprising that his interventions will, in some fashion, enhance the well-being of his own group, even if such consequences are not intended nor devious. He knows his own people best and can express their situation and needs. Status differentials, by definition, indicate to those within the social system that some people are more important than others, likely more valuable if resources are limited.

Of course the power imbalances present in the delivery of humanitarian assistance and immediate relief within complex emergencies are, in stark reality, simply there. People are basically powerless to provide for their own, possibly life-threatening, needs; the humanitarian relief system has the resources—material and human—for immediate response to the most pressing of these needs. Given the very real situation of a complex emergency, there is no way around that. It is how basic life services and ongoing medical, educational and economic aid are provided. Given the power differentials embedded in the humanitarian relief system, the typical approach is to maintain control over the refugees rather than consulting them as responsible equals (Harrell-Bond 1999).[6] It is here—in sharing responsibility in identifying issues, in decision making and in planning responses that allowing the refugees as much control over their lives as possible—that addresses some of the power imbalance. Emphasizing community participation—for example, in accessing health status, linking to community healers, involving community leaders and developing refugee health teams—is an approach that turns as much control as possible over to the refugees (MacArthur et al. 2000). The implication is that humanitarian aid workers should use human rights as a measure of their work.

Anthropologists and other social scientists, as members of teams or as researchers, can be invaluable resources for information and advocacy regarding the consequences of power imbalances. Power differentials are a social universal not unique to mass population displacements. In a complex emergency, the responding agencies must identify which of these differentials are affecting the delivery of aid, the planning of services and the protection of individuals in such a way as to jeopardize particular groups of people. As people experiencing severe displacement are dependent upon those providing relief, it is especially incumbent upon those providers to be aware of power differentials. At times, that means being self-aware and self-critical. Social scientists who recognize the intense pressures and often overwhelming responsibilities of the aid teams and, at the same time, have the skills to identify and analyze social power differentials within the displaced communities and between those communities and the aid workers, can provide insights and suggestions for ameliorating the conditions that increase risk and threaten human rights.

Protection

Protection is basic to human rights: It is the first priority (Toole and Waldman 1997). The various humanitarian responses in a complex emergency are protection from the terror and threats causing the flight.

People are often threatened, intimidated, and hurt, yet many times the displaced find it difficult to express these fears or talk with strangers: "Who are you?" and "Why do you want to talk with me?" Such fear was pervasive in Goma camp with Rwandan refugees and in the Cambodian border camps in Thailand controlled by the Khmer Rouge.

Unfortunately, protection concerns follow people into areas of refuge. Problems can come in the form of infiltrators from the country of origin or refuge. The fear of such persons is pervasive in mass displacement and settlement. Lack of trust is rampant, and for good reason.

As the Burmese military launched an offensive against the Karenni, mortar shells fell close to one of the refugee camps located in Thailand. Since the camp was situated very close to the border, the refugees fled deeper into Thai territory for safety. The local Thai officials, reluctant to have the camp relocate further inland, dispersed a militia group to relocate the camp to an area 5 kilometers from the border and close to a Burmese army encampment. When the Karenni refused to move to an area they felt to be unsafe, the militia threatened to kill the refugees. They emphasized these threats by beating on the walls of the houses with their rifles. [MacArthur 1995]

The political nature of mass displacement often means that there are opposing factions within a refugee camp. UNHCR attempts to keep arms and armed groups out of camps, often by setting up locked camps and monitoring who comes in and out. However, in a rapid, mass displacement such as the arrival of 10,000 Rwandan refugees daily into the camp at Goma in 1994, the systems were overwhelmed. In Goma, the very persons who had participated in the slaughter of Tutsis and moderate Hutus were in the camp with arms. When there are threats to protection at this level, the situation is beyond the scope of humanitarian relief agencies and must be dealt with at the state and multinational levels.

Sometimes protection problems are based in hostility between different ethnic or religious groups:

> Somalis were pouring into Kenya, over land and by sea. Those coming in small boats landed near Mombassa on the Indian Ocean. There were two camps, one in a rural area and one housed at an abandoned school right in the heart of Mombassa. The school-based camp, with space for only a few hundred persons, had people coming in steadily over a period of several days. UNHCR had not even had time to register them, to know much about them. As we walked through the camp a woman ran up to us, a mixture of anger and fear on her face, almost screaming in her attempt to communicate with us. She was a member of one clan; all the other people in the school were from another, rival clan. They were threatening her, preventing her from getting food and water, pushing and shoving her. She was hysterical with fear. [McSpadden 1992]

In camps housing Kosovar refugees, Roma refugees were threatened and assaulted. Although oppressed minorities themselves, they were accused by the Kosovo Albanians of joining with the Serbs in the destruction of homes, killing, and threats.

Sometimes camp authorities, wielding significant power, can use that power for their own benefit or for political ends. Physical threats are not uncommon. If there is hostility or suspicion on the part of the host country towards the refugees, the camp authorities become representatives of possible threat.

> Sitting in a small hut that had been turned into a little café, we drank warm cokes and talked with Ethiopian refugees who were planning to start a school for young children. The conversation was animated. Suddenly people fell silent; my colleague leaned over and said "Don't say anything more; just talk about nothing." I looked up and saw that a Kenyan, a camp staff, had entered the café. Apparently, he had been following us around the camp noting with whom we talked. We began to talk among ourselves, ignoring the refugees so as not to cause them problems. [McSpadden 1992]

Access to Resources

Necessities basic for life are essential resources: water, food, shelter, and medicine. Organizing access is a major task of the camp administration and humanitarian relief agencies, requiring intricate planning and well-coordinated efforts among UN agencies, NGOs, and state authorities. Public health and relief agencies' policies can directly affect the human rights of the population. Not only can establishing security measures assure protection, but also developing public health interventions with a human rights perspective can further protect the population from abuse. For example, ensuring the quantity and quality of food and water is necessary; however, making them available to everyone is another matter (Prothero 1994). Incorporating this perspective into the planning heightens awareness of vulnerable populations and thus strategies aimed at overcoming barriers may be developed.

In spite of the desire to give refugees an active role in the planning and implementation of relief programs, caution is essential. Camp staff from the host country or refugee leaders may control food distribution and other resources and benefits.[7] They may demand payment of money, sexual favors, or support of particular political activities (UNHCR 1999).

> The refugee camp was located far enough away from a trading center that supplies—food, medicine, clothing, basic living needs—had to be trucked in daily. Driving to the camp one day we happened to follow directly behind a supply truck as it pulled up to the gate of the locked camp. The camp guard held out his hand to the driver, obviously expecting a "financial donation" in order to open the gate. Seeing us watching him, he suddenly pulled his hand back and waved the truck through. [McSpadden 1992]

The physical realities of getting resources, especially food and water, can threaten the health, psychological and physical well-being of vulnerable persons. In households with only one healthy or strong adult, the rest of the household—elderly, children, incapacitated—must depend on that one person. If this person weakens or is denied access to food, medicine or other necessities through intimidation, discriminatory practices, or ineffective organization of service delivery, the basic well-being of all members is threatened. A subtle and deleterious factor in delivering health care is the frequent demeaning behavior of well-educated medical personnel towards persons who are illiterate and/or rural people.

The internal power relations within households themselves affect access to resources. These power relations are typically structured according to cultural mores and vary from group to group. Who is expected to gather the food? Who is entitled to eat first and most? Who shares with whom and why? If there is not enough food, what happens? Analyzing such dynamics in order to ameliorate the inequities is a major contribution of the anthropologist.

One of the most effective ways to identify problems regarding access to resources is to encourage the refugees to organize themselves, and have meetings to address the problems (UNHCR 1999). However, in so doing, some marginalized groups will continue to be ignored by those in power. Anthropologists can identify such people and groups; separate meetings can be arranged, for example, for groups of women who are heads of households or for unaccompanied minors.

The Rights of the Host Community

The Right to Food, Shelter, and Health Care

CHEs often occur quickly with large numbers of persons becoming displaced from the security of their homes. These people are not able to carry many personal items and often travel far distances with little food and water. Hunger, thirst, exposure, abuse, and disease all contribute to poor health upon arrival to the host country.

When tens of thousands of fleeing persons cross an international border and settle in an encampment, the degree of disruption on the local community can be devastating. The sociopolitical and economic relationships in frontier regions are not capable of withstanding such an influx of human beings. Because the host country is often poor, there are few local resources to provide assistance to the population of concern. Thus, in order to ensure that the basic needs of the displaced persons are met, an outpouring of international relief efforts follows. When international aid arrives, the need for vehicles, office space, food, and building supplies increases tremendously. With the increase in demand, there follows the obvious increase in prices. This can have a devastating affect on the local population.

With the outpouring of large funds for assistance programs, the basic needs of the refugees are met and the mortality falls. When death rates drop, the humanitarian emergency progresses into a maintenance phase that relief agencies describe as the relief to development continuum (Demusz 1998). Other projects develop during this phase, such as capacity building by training of essential personnel (for example, medics, nurses, health educators, teachers), elaborate water and sanitation projects and microenterprises. Each of these is aimed at producing a "self-sustainable" refugee. In certain situations, the relief efforts go far beyond what is available in the country of origin and/or refuge, and exceeds what will be available if/when repatriation occurs.

Article 25 of the *Universal Declaration of Human Rights* states that "everyone has the right to a standard of living adequate for the health and well-being of himself and of his family, including food, clothing, housing, and medical care" (UN 1948:8). The response of the international community to aid refugees and internally displaced persons addresses this right. Although these efforts are substantial and often done with the best of intentions, one must question the ethics of establishing programs that will create aid dependency.

Aid brings another problem as well. If the local community is poor, as is often the case, they lack many of the very basic needs that the refugee community lacks: food, water, security, and shelter. Unfortunately, it is not always easy to include the local community into the budget submitted to the donor nations. Thus, either the local villagers are completely left out of the aid process or merely given token gestures of support. This creates an imbalance in the distribution of resources and may build feelings of tremendous resentment on the part of the host community, leading to subsequent political problems and even hostilities.

When addressing the relief needs of the displaced community, it is imperative to be aware of the socioeconomic situation of the refugee's country of origin and the host villagers. A human rights perspective to relief ensures that both the refugees and the host villages have access to adequate health care, food, clothing and shelter. All efforts should be made to not only focus efforts on the displaced population, but also on the often-neglected villagers surrounding the refugee camps.

Gender

Although taking gender into consideration when planning for the delivery of humanitarian aid has been accepted as necessary, it would seem that operationalizing a gender perspective is typically problematical, since it requires "transforming the protection agenda itself" (Minear 1999). Some of this difficulty is because of a lack of understanding of what one means when talking about gender as significant factor in the provision of humanitarian aid.

Women and Men: Social Relationships and Power

A gender perspective requires analyzing how social power and responsibility are differentially constructed for men and women within a given society or cultural group. A gender focus necessitates that the different needs, vulnerabilities and capacities of women and men be recognized and responded to specifically or programmatically (Indra 1999). At its best, this approach helps us to put into focus inequalities involving both women and men. When gender inequities are faced, humanitarian aid workers are often challenged by the socially powerful to overlook the consequences of such inequities. Those who benefit frequently insist that "our cultural values must be honored; you have no right as an outsider to question our values." However, a commitment to protect human rights requires that the safety and dignity of the person be protected, even if this means challenging accepted cultural norms. Anthropologists, especially those with culture specific knowledge, have much to contribute in identifying the issues and guiding effective responses to protect and provide for vulnerable persons, both women and men.

Gender Inequities and Humanitarian Aid

Typically, a society is structured so that women have less access to resources and social power. Within the domain of humanitarian aid "most assistance is camp administered and most administrators are men" (Harrell-Bond 1999:40–62). When a gender focus was introduced into humanitarian aid delivery (Women in Development 1972), women in greatest need were the targets; for example, food was not distributed to the poorest of women. This was an "add women and stir" approach; there were no questions about power relations (Indra 1999).

With a power relationship focus, there is now more attention to social justice and the improvement of the quality of life for women and men. For example, an approach to household analysis would not assume that all persons benefit equally when food aid, medicine or tools are distributed to families. One would look at internal power relations in the family and ask how needs are met, keeping in mind that most of the "vulnerable groups" of concern—young children, elderly, the severely ill—are in the care of women. Harrell-Bond (1999) reports situations in which, when women in camps were given control over ration distribution, the system worked out more fairly (Harrell-Bond 1999).

Women sometimes have wider social networks than men; the consequence can be that in a complex emergency with limited resources, male-headed households could be worse off than female-headed households:

> The camp system was being overwhelmed by the daily, almost hourly arrival of hundreds of Somalis. There was not enough staff; the sanitary facilities were inadequate; shelter had not yet been constructed. In the corner of a crowded room a man sat with a three month old baby in his arms and a four year old daughter by his side. His wife had died two hours before; he was sitting and staring into space. Some women in the room were preparing food; children were running around. He seemed to be unnoticed. The baby will die, it is clear. [McSpadden 1992]

Women and Girls Have Special Health and Protection Needs

Without question, refugee women and girls have special health and protection needs.[8] Women, particularly those of childbearing age, will likely need preferential access to medical services in order to provide an "integrated package of growth monitoring, immunization, antenatal and postnatal care, treatment of common ailments, and health promotion" (Toole and Waldman 1997:307). For example, Gilles et al. (1969) describes malaria as a major cause of maternal mortality, abortion, stillbirths, premature birth, and low birth weight babies, thus special programs aimed at reducing malaria in pregnancy should be developed.

Consistent sexual vulnerability is the reality for women and girls in complex emergencies. Women and girls may experience physical and sexual attacks and abuse even after arriving at the camp. UNHCR, for example, reported 192 cases of rape of Somali refugee women in Kenyan camps over a seven-month period in 1993, and estimated that several thousand more rape cases went unreported (Toole and Waldman 1997). The basic layout of the camp again and again is a health-related factor that affects the safety of women: distance to latrines, lighting, and clearing of shrubs that obscure visibility and encourage rape (UNHCR 1995a).

Refugee women who are unable to feed, clothe, and shelter themselves and their children are more vulnerable to manipulation and to physical and sexual abuse.

If monetary bribes are necessary in order to get water or food, as was reported by Ethiopian refugees in camps in Djbouti, women will predictably experience sexual harassment. Reports consistently indicate that women are forced into prostitution to get life necessities for themselves and for their children (Moussa 1993). Domestic violence often increases in camps as men, having lost status and control over their lives, take out their anger on their wives and children.

> As we walked into Utunge camp near Mombassa, we saw persons huddled under trees. The UNHCR staff said the refugees were arriving in such large numbers that there were not enough blue tents to shelter them. In the distance were huts that the earlier arrivals had built. As we walked on, a Somali woman rushed up to the UNHCR staff woman and began to complain loudly. The UNHCR staff, a Pakistani woman, turned to the men gathered around watching and asked them to translate for the woman. No one responded; the woman continued to press her dilemma. Again the staff asked the men to translate. Finally one did. It seemed that the woman had been given a tent for herself and her children, but the tent had been taken away by some of the men. She was without shelter. No wonder the men did not want to translate! [McSpadden 1992]

All of these are issues of well-being, health, safety, and life resources. Sexual assault and endangerment, in addition, are issues of respect and dignity. Given the sensitivity of sexual issues and the continued threat when rape or other sexual harassment is revealed while the perpetrators are still present, it is essential that women staff or women social scientists be used when discussing this with the refugee women.

In addition, consulting with women regarding the realities of camp life, such as the type and location of water points, the location and means of collecting fuel for cooking and heating, the distribution of food, and the location of basic services such as latrines or medical facilities, is needed for protection. Men cannot speak for women. Participation of the women, especially in groups, is a process that promotes dignity and protection (UNHCR 1999).

In summary, a gender perspective involves social relationships and responsibilities of both men and women. Often one is more powerful or more "valued" in the culture; frequently, but not always, this is the man. Consistently, the less powerful are at risk. Men typically have the responsibility to care for, provide for and protect all the members of their families. However, in complex emergencies, the men frequently cannot carry out these responsibilities, resulting in psychological distress for the men, domestic abuse, and/or women assuming new responsibilities in addition to their normal ones. Most often, women have the responsibilities for the care of children, elderly, and the infirm, all of who have special needs. In addition, women have special reproductive health needs that are exacerbated by their vulnerability to sexual harassment and rape. Underlying all these is the differential valuation of women and men within a specific cultural context. Those who are less valued are at increased risk.

Interviewing Survivors of Human Rights Abuse

Refugees can be traumatized by both abuse suffered in their home country and/or the effects of forced migration (Basoglu et al. 1994; Holtz 1998). Those conducting interviews in this population should be aware of how the population became displaced, the psychological sequelae survivors may have, interviewing techniques, possible interventions, and recognizing interviewer countertransference.

Process of Torture/Human Rights Abuses

Many displaced people have suffered extreme human rights abuses, including torture. The 20th century has seen torture reemerge as a tool of authoritarian states. Up to 35 percent of world's refugees have experienced torture. It is one of the most severe forms of human rights abuse that can lead to profound psychological sequelae (Baker 1992).

Torture is a sociopolitical phenomenon. It is often, but not always, aimed at the destruction of enemies of the state. Through the detention and abuse of the prisoner, the state acts to inflict societal trauma. Often the person abducted and tortured holds a position of respect in the community. The aim of the torturer is not to kill the victim, but rather to subject them to dehumanizing experiences. The survivor of torture may then be released, sending reverberations throughout the community and effectively communicating the message of what happens if one goes counter to the wishes of the captors.

Weinstein and colleagues have developed a list of risk factors for having been tortured that can be applied to refugees or displaced persons (Weinstein et al. 1996). Those working in communities with the following characteristics should be alerted to the possibility that some of the members may have been tortured.

- Refugee comes from country with totalitarian history
- Member of minority group in country of origin
- Member of minority political party in country of origin
- Civil war in country of origin

- Residence in refugee camp
- Military government in country of origin
- Prisoner of war in high-conflict country
- Multiple family members deceased because of trauma
- History of arrest or detention
- Leadership in an antigovernment organization or relative of same

Many of these characteristics may also be used as an early warning system alerting the international community of impending humanitarian crises. When these are present, the population may be close to making the decision to flee in search of protection.

The Nature of Flight

The decision to leave one's home does not come easily and is often influenced by a complex set of circumstances. Prior to fleeing, torture survivors live in a state of unrest and insecurity. They experience upheaval of their families, homes and communities and the loss of previous societal roles and status. The survivor often arrives at an international border with very few personal belongings; upon crossing the border they "officially" become refugees. Loss of material items compounds their feelings of despair. The nature of the journey may include fear of discovery, hunger, further torture, rape, robbery, disease, and other difficulties adding to their overall psychological stress. Often on arrival, the new site for a refuge camp is still not secure, there may be resentment on behalf of the host country and the refugee must confront linguistic, financial, and cultural obstacles (Cunningham et al. 1990).

Psychological Effects

It is important for the social scientist not only to recognize the reasons for flight but also to acquaint themselves with some of the potential psychological manifestations of either surviving torture or other human rights abuses.

Psychological sequelae can manifest themselves in a variety of ways. Cultural differences may lead to variability in how these symptoms present. Thus, the symptoms may present as somatic complaints including abdominal pain, nervousness, insomnia, chest pain, weakness, poor appetite, diarrhea, numbness, and sweating. Often underlying depression and anxiety appear.

Behavior changes are commonly seen as well. The absence of family members, friends or other persons of the survivor's former support system often exacerbate societal withdrawal. Other symptoms experienced are exaggerated startle response to loud noises, fear of authority figures, aggressive behavior, reexperiencing the event, nightmares, and suicidal ideation. Some survivors may also experience cognitive difficulties. Because many people may have experienced physical blows to the head, some of these symptoms may be because of organic pathology and not merely psychological manifestations of the abuse.

In order to protect themselves from recurrent memories of the torture experience, the survivor will often employ some form of defense mechanisms. These assist the survivor in avoiding feelings of helplessness, shame and guilt. Amnesia of the event is the most severe manifestation of these types of defense mechanisms.

Interviewing Survivors

The interview process in a CHE can vary depending on the objective of the project. The relief agency might ask a social scientist to assist in further understanding the nature of the refugees' belief system. This information will allow the agency to adopt culturally specific and appropriate interventions in such areas as public health, education, capacity building, or job skills training. The interviewing used to gather this information must be done with utmost sensitivity. Certain interviewing styles may lead to reexperiencing an interrogation that occurred during the torture.

Many survivors are reluctant to recount their torture experiences. Fear of not being believed, shame to reveal the profound depth of the violations experienced and defense mechanisms all contribute to their reluctance (Chester and Holtan 1992). Often the interviewer must use an interpreter to assist in conducting the interviews. This may further act to suppress the survivor's desire to discuss the torture. Even though the survivor and the interpreter may share a similar language, there may be differences in ethnicity, religion, class, educational levels, and previous societal standing in the community (Faust and Drickey 1986).

Although many survivors of human rights abuses are reluctant to speak of their experiences, others want the world to know of what is occurring in their homeland. These individuals are very willing to speak to the interviewer about their experiences and look to the foreign relief worker to "bear witness" of the events. They may even actively seek the interviewer out in order to relay the experience.

Reluctance to investigate the human rights abuse stemming from concern that in-depth questions will retraumatize the refugee often occurs. Because the torture survivor can harbor a profound lack of trust for any person in a position of power, it is better not to attempt to illicit torture testimony from a person who is not freely speaking. It is difficult to foster trust over the course of a brief interview. However, if the survivor is willing and interested in recounting the history, the process of retelling may be therapeutic. One aim of the torturer is keeping the survivor from speaking about the experience, often saying that nobody will care what happens to him or her. They want the person to be haunted by memories of the events for life. It is imperative that the interview is always constructed in such a manner as to allow the survivor to set acceptable parameters, rules, and expectations of the process.

Interventions to Regain Control

The role of the social scientist in complex emergencies is multifaceted (see MacArthur et al. this bulletin). Relief workers with a human rights perspective can be advocates for the displaced population. Awareness and sensitivity to both the culture of relief agencies and displaced populations allows for urging the inclusion of human rights into all aspects of programmatic planning and implementation.

Although mental health disorders are among the leading medical problems in refugee situations, it is rare to find mental health professionals as a part of the initial relief team. While social scientists are not trained in psychological assessment and intervention, there are techniques that can be employed to assist a survivor of torture. A safe, predictable environment with available, culturally appropriate social support will enhance the recovery process. Provision of other basic needs such as protection, shelter, food, water and medical care is also important. Since the nature of torture is to isolate the individual and to place them in an uncontrollable situation, intervention efforts should be aimed at allowing the survivor to regain control over his or her life. Allowing him or her to exert control will improve upon their negative self-perception and contribute to the healing process.

Interviewer's Personal Feelings/Countertransference

When involved in a large assessment of a displaced population where the population has been exposed to a tremendous level of human rights abuse, the interviewer may find the experience emotionally overwhelming. Not only is the work exhausting, often lasting 12 or more hours a day for multiple days, the interviewing process often exposes the interviewer to stories that go beyond the realm of what society would classify as normal human experiences. This can lead to secondary trauma in the persons taking the abuse histories. Countertransference, defined as certain actions by the interviewer to satisfy his or her own unconscious needs and feelings towards the patient, has been observed in work with torture survivors (Bustos 1990). Major paradigms of countertransference in psychoanalysis include avoidance/withdrawal, helplessness/hopelessness, anger/sadistic feelings, viewing the survivor as a hero, shame, privileged voyeurism, and overidentification (Danieli 1984; Danskey 1993). All of these lead to a general loss of objectivity. If the interviewer is aware of these potential problems and seeks avenues for the expression of their own feelings about what they are listening to, their own trauma may be minimized.

Roles for the Anthropologist

Protection is the foundational human rights issue. For protection to be effective, information is necessary. Gathering such information requires sensitivity to the life-threatening and respect-demeaning conditions faced by the refugees. Awareness of the possibilities of human rights abuses is necessary. These abuses may be embedded within the system, because of the system being overwhelmed or a lack of understanding of the issues on the part of those controlling the system. In bringing such abuses to light and analyzing their causes anthropologists can be effective advocates for protecting human rights.

The anthropologist possesses special training in assessing and understanding the cultural value system, as well as the social networks that comprise a community. Given the centrality of value systems and the sensitivity of social networks for persons in life-threatening situations, protection and human rights issues are especially important when carrying out research on vulnerable populations—displaced persons and host communities—within a complex emergency. The information gathering process must protect the rights of these people, whether by means of improving their access to needed resources, protecting them from violence or intimidation or advocating for specific changes within the humanitarian system of aid delivery itself. The anthropologist has an obligation to design and carry out the research with such goals in mind. Researchers must communicate clearly with the people being interviewed how the information will be used. This allows for control and protection; such an approach will also enhance collaboration and likely increase the quality of the research itself.

In order to be effective in the context of a complex emergency, social scientists should widen their perspectives and attempt to look at the refugees' needs without the traditional rural development biases. It is crucial to have the vision to see beyond what the donor nations want, to resist writing the grant proposal merely because there is money to spend and to forecast the repatriation process. Advocating programmatic approaches that minimize dependency and highlight the needs of the local villagers are all critical aspects of what can be offered by a social scientist that has insights into the cultures of the refugees, the host community and the relief agencies.

It is equally important to become well informed about the demands upon humanitarian aid staff: their responsibilities, authority, and limits. The ability to carry out human rights-focused research can be an enormous contribution to overextended staff operating under intense time frames. The literature is replete with assertions that data necessary for planning appropriate public health interventions are often lacking; for example, morbidity and mortality data of displaced women.[9] There are numerous calls for the well-planned pursuit of answers to many important questions, as well as for the sharing of such information with key organizations, in order to enhance cooperation and delivery of services. Social scientists, especially medical anthropologists, are trained, and as members of a team, well positioned to contribute to these needs. Even within a complex emergency there are ways of protecting the lives of vulnerable people. Social scientists can contribute significantly to identifying points of threat to human rights; ones that must not be ignored any more than one would consider ignoring the absence of water, food, and shelter. Social scientists should take a major role to ensure effective protection.

Notes

Disclaimer. The views expressed within this chapter are solely those of the authors and do not reflect those of the United States Public Health Service, the United States Department of Health and Human Services, or the Life and Peace Institute.

Acknowledgments. The authors wish to thank Holly Ann Williams for her insightful comments into the preparation of this manuscript. Dr. MacArthur is especially grateful to the late Dr. Jonathan Mann who served as friend, mentor, and inspiration to an entire generation of young professionals dedicated to the field of health and human rights; he is dearly missed.

1. The number of refugees and internally displaced persons is always contentious. Because of national concerns or government denial of access to UNHCR and other agencies, the number is assumed to be much higher than reported here.

2. Complex emergencies involve persons fleeing a variety of life-threatening circumstances. However, under international law, for example the 1951 UN Convention Relating to the Status of Refugees and its 1967 Protocol, only those persons fleeing because of "a well-founded fear of being persecuted for reasons of race, religion, nationality, membership of a particular social groups or political opinion" are recognized as bona fide refugees and hence entitled to international protection as refugees. (See Ferris 1993 for a thorough discussion of the complexities and consequences of such international distinctions.)

3. Social scientists from a variety of disciplines, (e.g., sociologists, political scientists, and educators), may also find themselves in the midst of teams working in complex emergencies. The authors would hope that such persons would find the reflections contained here, aimed at anthropologists with specific training in field techniques and cultural analysis, to be useful.

4. A complete listing of human rights related UN conventions is found on the UN High Commissioner for Human Rights web page, www.unhchr.ch.

5. That there are other factors that affect human rights in complex emergencies is clear. We have chosen those factors to which social scientists may be able to bring particular expertise in such a way as to enhance and protect the human rights of the displaced.

6. Barbara Harrell-Bond's (1986) controversial and challenging book, *Imposing Aid: Emergency Assistance to Refugees,* continues to be a seminal work critiquing the international humanitarian response system and one with which all aid workers would do well to be familiar.

7. An egregious example is when the leaders of the former Hutu-controlled Rwandan government took control of distributing relief supplies in the refugee camps in Zaire (Democratic Republic of the Congo) in 1994. The result was that these supplies ended up with men of the former Rwandan Army resulting in elevated malnutrition rates among children in female-headed households.

8. Surprisingly, however, "in most emergency situations, gender-specific mortality data has not been collected . . . [although] a number of authors have described increased risk of both morbidity and mortality among women in refugee and displaced populations" (Toole and Waldman 1997:292).

9. Reporting on a recent World Health Organization inventory of research in humanitarian settings, (Waldman and Martone 1999) note that it is remarkable for its sparseness, not for any wealth of information.

References Cited

Baker, Ron
 1992 Psychosocial Consequences for Tortured Refugees Seeking Asylum and Refugee Status in Europe. *In* Torture and Its Consequences: Current Treatment and Approaches. Metin Basoglu, ed. Pp. 83–106. New York: Cambridge University Press.
Basoglu, Metin
 1993 Prevention of Torture and Care of Survivors: An Integrated Approach. Journal of the American Medical Association 270(5):606–611.
Basoglu, Metin, M. Parker, O. Parker, E. Ozmen, I. Marks, C. Incesu, D. Sahin, and N. Sarimurat
 1994 Psychological Effects of Torture: A Comparison of Tortured with Nontortured Political Activists in Turkey. American Journal of Psychiatry 151(1):76–81.
Bustos, E.
 1990 Dealing with the Unbearable: Reactions of Therapists and Therapeutic Institutions to Survivors of Torture. *In* Torture and Psychology. Peter Suedfeld, ed. Pp. 143–163. New York: Hemisphere Publishing Corporation.
Chester, Barbara, and Neal Holtan
 1992 Working with Refugee Survivors of Torture. Western Journal of Medicine 157(3):301–304.
Cunningham, Margaret, Derrick Silove, and Victor Storm
 1990 Counseling Survivors of Torture and Refugee Trauma. Australian Family Physician 19(4):501–504, 506, 509–510.
Danieli, Y.
 1984 Psychotherapist's Participation in the Conspiracy of Silence about the Holocaust. Psychoanalytical Psychology 1:231–244.
Danskey, Laura
 1993 Barriers to the Recognition and Treatment of Survivors. Abstract. San Francisco: American Public Health Association Annual Conference.
Demusz, Kerry
 1998 From Relief to Development: Negotiating the Continuum on the Thai-Burmese Border. Journal of Refugee Studies 11(3):231–244.
Dick, Bruce, and Stephanie Simmonds
 1983 Refugee Health Care: Similar but Different? Disasters 7(4):291–303.
Faust, Shotsy, and Robert Drickey
 1986 Working with Interpreters. Journal of Family Practice 22(2):131,134–138.
Ferris, Elizabeth G.
 1993 Beyond Borders: Refugees, Migrants and Human Rights in the Post-Cold War Era. Geneva: World Council of Churches.
Gilles, H. M., J. B. Lawson, M. Sibelas, A. Voller, and N. Allan
 1969 Malaria, Anaemia and Pregnancy. Annals of Tropical Medicine and Parasitology 63(2):245–63.
Harrell-Bond, Barbara E.
 1986 Imposing Aid: Emergency Assistance to Refugees. Oxford: Oxford University Press.
 1999 Interview with Barbara Harrell-Bond. *In* Engendering Forced Migration: Theory and Practice. Doreen Indra, ed. Pp. 40–62. New York: Berghahn Books.
Holtz, Timothy H.
 1998 Refugee Trauma Versus Torture Trauma: A Retrospective Controlled Cohort Study of Tibetan Refugees. Journal of Nervous and Mental Disease 186(1):24–34.
Indra, Doreen
 1999 Not a 'Room of One's Own': Engendering Forced Migration Knowledge and Practice. *In* Engendering Forced Migration. Doreen Indra, ed. Pp. 1–22. New York: Berghahn Books.
Institute of Medicine
 1988 Future of Public Health. Washington, DC: National Academy Press.
Kyi, Aung San Suu
 1991 Freedom from Fear. London: Penguin Books.
MacArthur, John R.
 1995 Field Notes. Unpublished MS, International Rescue Committee, Thailand.

MacArthur, John R., Holly A. Williams, and Peter B. Bloland
    2000 Malaria Control in Complex Humanitarian Emergencies. Refuge 18(5):4–10.
Mann, Jonathan M., Lawrence Gostin, Sofia Gruskin, Troyen Brennan, Zita Lazzarini, and
Harvey V. Fineberg
    1994 Health and Human Rights. Health and Human Rights 1(1):6–23.
McSpadden, Lucia Ann
    1992 Refugee Camps in Kenya: A Report to Church World Service. New York: Church
        World Service.
McSpadden, Lucia Ann, and Ayok A. Chol
    1998 Generating the Political Will for Protecting the Rights of Refugees. In The Future of
        the United Nations System: Potential for the Twenty First Century. C. F. Alger, ed. Pp.
        282–314. Tokyo: United Nations University Press.
Minear, Larry
    1999 Partnerships in the Protection of Refugees and Other People at Risk: Emerging Is-
        sues and Work in Progress. In New Issues in Refugee Research. Geneva: UNHCR Cen-
        tre for Documentation and Research.
Moussa, Helene
    1993 Storm and Sanctuary: The Journey of Ethiopian and Eritrean Women Refugees.
        Dundas: Artemis Enterprises.
Prothero, R. Mansell
    1994 Forced Movements of Population and Health Hazards in Tropical Africa. Interna-
        tional Journal of Epidemiology 23(4):657–664.
Toole, Michael J., and Ronald J. Waldman
    1997 The Public Health Aspects of Complex Emergencies and Refugee Situations. An-
        nual Review of Public Health 18:283–312.
United Nations
    1948 Universal Declaration of Human Rights. In Twenty-Five Human Rights Documents.
        Center for the Study of Human Rights, ed. Pp. 6–9. New York: Columbia University.
United Nations High Commissioner for Refugees
    1995a Sexual Violence against Refugees: Guidelines on Prevention and Response. Ge-
        neva: UNHCR.
    1995b The State of the World's Refugees: In Search of Solutions. London: Oxford Univer-
        sity Press.
    1999 Protecting Refugees: A Field Guide for NGOs. Geneva: UNHCR.
U.S. Committee for Refugees
    2000 World Refugee Survey 2000. Washington, DC: USCR.
Waldman, Ronald, and Gerald Martone
    1999 Public Health and Complex Emergencies: New Issues, New Conditions. American
        Journal of Public Health 89(10):1483–1485.
Weinstein, Harvey M., Laura Dansky, and Vincent Iacopino
    1996 Torture and War Trauma Survivors in Primary Care Practice. Western Journal of
        Medicine 165(3):112–128.

CHAPTER 4

Approaches to Facilitating Health Care Acceptance: A Case Example from Karenni Refugees

John R. MacArthur
Malaria Epidemiology Branch, Division of Parasitic Diseases, National Center for Infectious Diseases, Centers for Disease Control and Prevention

Sandra Dudley
Jesus College, University of Oxford

Holly Ann Williams
Malaria Epidemiology Branch, Division of Parasitic Diseases, National Center for Infectious Diseases, Centers for Disease Control and Prevention

As of the end of 1999, there were an estimated 35 million persons uprooted by war, famine, civil conflict, and political persecution, and classified as refugees or displaced persons (U.S. Committee for Refugees 2000).[1,2] The process of displacement has a tremendous impact on the health, social and cultural well-being of those affected, as well as on host communities. In the acute phase of a complex emergency, mortality rates are very high, resulting mainly from communicable diseases, malnutrition, and war-related trauma (Toole and Waldman 1990, 1993). Because of this high mortality rate, humanitarian agencies initially focus attention on meeting basic needs, such as clean water, food, shelter, and the control of infectious diseases and epidemics. Although this focus is critical, particularly in the initial phases of a complex emergency, sociocultural aspects of the experience of displacement are often neglected. Yet, displaced persons are often confronted with significant dissonance between their own sociocultural patterns and those of the host community and international relief workers. In addition, the displaced population is frequently viewed as a single, homogeneous group; whereas, it may comprise more than one cultural group, each with its own ethnic and political identities. Such diversity is often a function of the displacement process. Furthermore, disruption of social networks during and after displacement may lead to feelings of isolation, inadequacy, and insecurity. These various stressors may manifest themselves at different times in the migration process.

The health of refugees should be examined within its broader cultural, socioeconomic and political contexts (Clinton-Davis and Fassil 1992). Persons forced to take flight carry with them a rich set of beliefs of health and illness, deeply rooted in their predisplacement cultural logic. Likewise, the staff of humanitarian relief organizations intervening in refugee emergencies bring their own cultural perspectives. Failure to recognize these differences prior to the design and implementation of public health projects can have serious implications.

Since 1991, the International Rescue Committee (IRC) has been providing relief services to Karenni refugees. From 1989 to the present, the number of Karenni fleeing into Thailand has continued to increase.[3] On arrival, they are confronted with an unfamiliar healthcare system and international relief workers of which the refugees have had little or no predisplacement experience. The extent of the cultural disparity between refugees and relief workers is, however, varied across the diverse refugee population. Similarly varied is the degree to which refugees differ from, and have impact on, each other.

This chapter discusses the exile experiences of a particular refugee community and explores one international relief agency's attempt to increase the acceptance of public health programs implemented during various phases of a complex emergency. This agency adopted several strategies to develop their understanding of the cultures of the refugees with whom they worked and, accordingly, to improve the cultural sensitivity and appropriateness of programs delivered.

Background

The Karenni

The Karenni are a mainly rural, diverse, non-Burman ethnic minority population from Karenni State in eastern Burma. They have sought refuge in substantial numbers in northwest Thailand since 1989 (see Figure 1). Their reasons for flight range from the acute experience of enforced village "relocation" to a gradual buildup of eventually intolerable violence and abuse. Some members of the Karenni social and political elite have principally fled in order to continue their opposition to the Burmese military regime. This elite comprises the Karenni National Progressive Party (KNPP), a political organization that argues that Karenni State is and always has been an independent territory occupied by an alien aggressor (the Burmese) since Burma's independence from Britain in 1948. The KNPP maintains an armed wing inside Karenni State that continues to resist the Burmese Army and operates a self-styled "government-in-exile" civil administration in the refugee camps. There are Karenni groups other than

Figure 1. Map of the Thai-Burma Border showing the location of the Kayah (Karenni) State and Refugee Camps.

the KNPP in opposition to the current Burmese government, but they are not currently engaged in armed conflict.

The term *Karenni* is used by the people to describe themselves, even though it includes up to eleven self-distinguishing ethnolinguistic groups. Karenni subgroups include the Kayah, various Kayan subgroups, the Kayaw, the Manu, the Yintale, and the Paku Karen.

In addition to their linguistic and ethnic diversity, the Karenni are heterogeneous in terms of socioeconomic class, educational background, religion, awareness of the wider world, political aspirations, and, in the refugee camps, the experience of displacement itself. Indeed, one of the main effects of Karenni displacement has been to bring together members of different Karenni State communities in the relatively small and confined spaces of the camps. Karenni refugees come from the same area of Burma and have varying degrees of shared history, ethnicity, and language. However, before displacement they had much less direct contact with and influence on each other. The process of becoming and being refugees has still further concentrated the Karenni's characteristic diversity.

Refugees in Thailand

Most Karenni refugees were displaced by the Burmese military regime's post-1988 commitment to eliminating the "ethnic problem" by increasing the frequency and severity of attacks in areas held by the insurgent armies. These military offensives have affected numerous villagers in multiple ethnic areas. The overall number of Burmese ethnic minority refugees in Thailand from 1985–89 remained relatively stable at approximately 20,000. However, the number had doubled by the end of 1989, tripled by 1991, and increased sixfold by 1997 (Burma Border Consortium n.d.). Most of these refugees come from non-Burman ethnic areas in the east of Burma. There are also smaller numbers of Burman and other students from urban centers who fled Burma after the regime's brutal suppression since 1988 of prodemocracy uprisings.

Most Burmese refugees in Thailand live in camps strung along the Thai-Burma border. Programs operated by relief agencies have been coordinated under the auspices of the Coordinating Committee for Services to Displaced Persons in Thailand (CCSDPT) and assorted refugee relief committees. The United Nations High Commissioner for Refugees (UNHCR) arrived on the border in 1998 and instituted a formal program of refugee registration.

Karenni Refugees

Karenni refugees mostly reside in three main camps in the northwestern Thai province of Mae Hong Son. By August 1999, there were 16,408 Karenni refugees in Thailand (Burma Border Consortium n.d.). Within the camps, the heterogeneity of the displaced population is well illustrated by the differences between many of the Karenni in residence in the camps before 1996 and new refugees who began to arrive in one particular Karenni camp from June 1996 onward. These new refugees were ethnically Kayah from a remote area of the Karenni State. While the Kayah are the majority ethnic group both in the Karenni State and in the preexisting refugee population, it was impossible not to be struck by the extraordinary differences between the new arrivals and the longer-staying refugee community.

The new arrivals were highly "traditional" in their culture, most obviously in female dress and religious and curative practices. Most claimed that before crossing the border they had rarely or never seen motor vehicles, let alone foreigners. In their homeland, they had little or no access to formal education or conventional healthcare. The longer-staying refugees, by contrast, were mostly Christian with a minority composed of Buddhist and followers of other traditional religions. These refugees had greater exposure to formal education and conventional healthcare. Among the political elite of the KNPP there are a number of persons with degrees from Burmese universities.

Furthermore, before becoming refugees, almost all new arrivals had little, if any, awareness of the KNPP and its political ideology and agenda. Their decision to flee to Thailand was a rapid response to intolerable violence and abuse, rather than a decision motivated by any political ideology or notion of revolution. The differences between the new arrivals and the longer-term camp residents led to the new arrivals having a particular set of problems in coping with their displacement.

Nongovernment Organization Assistance to Karenni Refugees

The first Karenni refugee camp was established in 1989. Early in the 1980s, the Royal Thai Government asked Médecins Sans Frontières (MSF), who were working in Cambodian refugee camps, to assist with newly arrived Karen refugees. When the Karenni entered Thailand, MSF, the only nongovernmental organization (NGO) established on the Thai-Burmese border at that time, responded to the crisis with medical aid. As the Burmese military offensives escalated against the ethnic groups, thousands more refugees followed. With these dramatic increases in refugees from Burma entering Thailand, and the length of the rugged border area where they settled, the emergency exceeded the capacity of MSF to effectively provide and monitor relief assistance. As a result, in 1991 MSF and the Karenni National Refugee Committee invited IRC to establish a medical relief program in the Karenni camps. After conducting a needs assessment and discussing options with the Karenni (KNPP) leadership, a small office was established in 1992. From the onset, IRC chose to focus on community-based and development-oriented programs (Demusz 1998). Early relief efforts consisted of basic primary health care, water and sanitation and distribution of food supplies.

IRC-Thailand recognized the need for the organization to undergo cross-cultural training. An annual retreat, facilitated by a Thai social scientist, was organized to improve the working relationship between Western and Asian staff and enhance the agency's relationships with the Karenni. Burmese language classes were also made available for the IRC field staff.

Three Approaches

The Role of Karenni Healthcare Workers

In planning health services to the newly displaced population, the KNPP and IRC chose Karenni to staff the refugee camp health centers. Once trained, they would serve as medics, nurses and laboratory technicians for the camp population. Young men and women were selected to undergo training conducted by various international relief organizations. Depending on the position, these refugees received up to two years of closely supervised training, usually by Western medical teams. This training provided education in medicine and exposure to Western relief workers. The instruction of these medical workers resulted in a body of skills developing within the refugee population (Demusz 1998). Importantly, this education met concerns held by both the KNPP and IRC that dependency on foreign assistance be kept to a minimum, both now and in the future (cf. Woodrow 1998).

Most of the medics were competent in English and often served as interpreters for agency staff and played an important role in planning and implementing almost all aspects of the relief efforts. Furthermore, as the IRC physician was only able to spend two to three days per month in any one camp, Karenni healthcare workers assumed roles of primary health providers. They often acted as crucial, close observers of shifts in disease patterns in the camps. For example, one camp medic noticed what he felt to be a dramatic increase in the number of malaria cases. He checked this by comparing the current numbers with the statistics for previous months and years, then alerted the IRC physician to his findings. Together, they confirmed an epidemic. Although the IRC team mobilized outside support, the medic met with community leaders to explain the situation. A coordinated response involving other NGOs, Karenni medical staff from other camps, women's groups, teachers, and religious leaders effectively encouraged the entire camp to be tested for malaria. As a result of this orchestrated effort, there were no deaths reported due to the outbreak.

IRC operated under the philosophy that minimal expatriate intervention was the most appropriate methodology for the implementation of public health programs. This was an attempt to build capacity within the Karenni medical community for possible self-sustainable projects once the refugees returned to their home villages (Woodrow 1998). One such program was training in Community Oriented Primary Care (COPC). The term COPC is a modification of the traditional primary health care (PHC) models. Whereas PHC is a generally comprehensive model providing essential health care, it has often lacked the component of population-based medicine. The IRC COPC project was designed to have the medics use epidemiologic data and coordinate with community members to develop health programs. The medics blended their own emic perspectives of what were considered important health problems with their knowledge of Western medicine and public health. In doing so, they sought to work closely with community members designing culturally appropriate and acceptable public health interventions.

There were challenges in using refugee health workers as links to the greater community. To qualify for training, these health workers needed to have at least a seventh-grade education level. This educational qualification restricted the applicants to those coming from the relatively privileged social class. This group was generally composed of Christian members of the KNPP. When interacting with IRC, the Karenni medical teams functioned within political and social confines dictated by the ruling elite. This reduced their ability to objectively convey information about the needs of the Karenni population to IRC members. For instance, when IRC gathered data on reproductive needs of the refugee community, the staff encountered numerous women who asked for assistance in planning their families. Others simply stated that they wanted no more children. However, when discussed with the medical staff and KNPP leaders, the message was clear that the Karenni were a small ethnic group and needed to grow; there was no need for family planning in the camps.

The Role of Burmese Relief Workers

In an effort to increase the cultural awareness and overall sensitivity of the Karenni relief program and to improve communication, IRC transferred a Burmese physician working in Lao refugee camps in Thailand to manage the Karenni health programs. This doctor had been exiled from Burma for treating wounded Burmese prodemocracy demonstrators in 1988. She had been identified as an enemy of the state and repeatedly interrogated and harassed by the Burmese military intelligence service.

A second prodemocracy exiled woman, half-Burman, half-ethnic Karen, later joined the IRC team as Health Liaison Officer (HLO). The role of HLO was to serve as a bridge between the new community health education program within IRC's programmatic structure and the Karenni leaders, health team and villagers. She had been a student leader in Rangoon during the uprisings of 1988, spent one year in Thailand as a refugee, and was the first Burmese to gain asylum in the United States. After finishing her university education, she returned to the border to assist the refugees.

As with the physician, this woman also had a history of struggles against the military regime. The presence of exiled, "antigovernment" Burmese workers seemed to be well accepted by many of the Karenni. Their common links of opposition to the Burmese regime and suffering at its hands, from a Karenni perspective, conferred legitimacy on the two individuals. In that sense, a bond of politics and suffering was able to transcend a normally stressful ethnic divide. Many Karenni, for example, use Burmese as a lingua franca, a fact that made communication with Burmese relief workers easy. The political and experiential bonds between the Karenni and these Burmese relief workers, together with their ability to speak a common language, allowed the two groups to work well together. As a result, the relationship between the KNPP and IRC also benefited.

IRC viewed these Burmese relief workers as facilitating a greater understanding of Karenni culture. There were strengths to using this strategy from both the Karenni and the NGO perspective. For example, the Burmese HLO, before starting with IRC, had lived in one of the Karenni refugee camps teaching in the school system. This had certainly strengthened her relationship with the community and provided her with additional insights into Karenni culture.

During joint meetings between Karenni leaders and IRC staff, which included the two Burmese, discussions about programmatic planning and community needs were often one sided. Community leaders often sat passively listening to IRC, yet rarely contributed to the discussion in spite of efforts by the NGO staff to elicit their concerns. However, when the Burmese workers and refugee community leaders met privately, fruitful discussions ensued and the Burmese staff was able to convey to the NGO information about community desires, needs, and suggestions.

The fact remained, however, that while both these Burmese workers contributed greatly to the cultural understanding of the refugees, they were not native to the ethnic community and, thus, their ability to fully bridge cultural gaps was somewhat limited. One problem was that Burmese is not spoken by many less educated Karenni. Furthermore, those who are less likely to speak Burmese are also less likely to have a wide political awareness of Burma as a whole, thus rendering the apparent bonds with Burmese relief workers less relevant.

Relationships with the NGO were also problematic from two perspectives. Full acceptance as objective cultural brokers was not possible because of the refugee community's perceived close identification of the Burmese workers with IRC. *Culture broker* is a concept used frequently in anthropology to describe an individual who is competent in two cultures and languages, whose purpose is to mediate or broker shared understandings and good relationships between the groups in order to work out problems or difficulties in a manner that is satisfactory to both sides (Dennis 1994). At the same time, the strength of the HLO relationship with the refugees was threatening to the NGO supervisors because of their inability to communicate directly with refugees. For example, the Community Health Education (CHE) students would seek out the HLO, rather than the supervisor, for information concerning most questions. The lack of direct communication with the Karenni led the supervisor to feel dissociated from the training and produced some degree of mistrust between herself and the HLO.

There were situations for both the physician and the HLO when the relationship with the refugee community prevented them from objectively analyzing situational needs. This, at times, produced a stressful environment when the organization chose relief strategies that the Burmese staff felt not to be responsive to the needs of the community.

Clearly, there are a number of risks in utilizing either ethnic refugees or others of similar backgrounds to act as cultural brokers (cf. Dennis 1994).

Nevertheless, in view of the difficulties, the relationship that the Burmese relief workers developed with the refugee community allowed the NGO to improve planning and implementation of public health projects. However, it was important for the non-Burmese NGO staff to comprehend the limitations of using these staff as cross-cultural brokers.

New Arrivals, New Traditions

The refugees who began to arrive in mid-1996 had walked four to seven days in the monsoon rains and mud, through dense forest and over mountains while avoiding the Burmese military. On arrival, many of them had not eaten for days and were suffering from exhaustion, malnutrition, malaria, respiratory infections, and diarrhea. The fatality rate in the refugee camps dramatically escalated during July and August 1996. By the beginning of August, the refugee camp had more than doubled in size and, by November, it had tripled. Conditions rapidly deteriorated, and great demands were placed upon available space, existing residents and IRC staff.

IRC was faced with a situation in which the relief situation had transformed from a stable, development-oriented maintenance phase setting to an acute-phase emergency. The organization was presented with a high influx of refugees originating from very remote areas of Karenni State. In view of this crisis and the noticeable differences between the newly arrived and more long-term Karenni refugees, IRC identified the need for ethnographic research to improve the cultural appropriateness of the delivery of relief services. The intention was both to ease the transition into refugee life of new arrivals and to increase the effectiveness of the public health programs.

A social anthropology doctoral student, already living in another Karenni camp undertaking field research, was requested by IRC to gather the needed data. She was not previously associated with IRC, nor was she a medical anthropologist. In addition, she received no remuneration from IRC and did not become a staff member. Without a formal linkage to the NGO, she had a greater degree of flexibility and independence in the research than might have been possible for an NGO staff member.[4]

For IRC, the primary objectives of the research were to provide information that would facilitate a greater understanding of the new arrivals' beliefs and practices concerning health and illness. Data pertaining to the following areas were also collected: traditional healers or medicines, culturally constituted notions of fertility, feeding preferences and taboos, family structures, household decision making, and the perceptions of the new refugees toward the health care services in the camp. The anthropologist structured informal interviews with new arrivals to address these issues, but for her the research related to her doctoral fieldwork—gathering qualitative ethnographic data pertaining to Kayah cultural identity and how it was affected by displacement (Dudley 1997).

Much of her report was well received and acted on. For example, one of the main research findings concerned the dynamics within the heterogeneous refugee community. The data revealed differences between the new arrivals and the previously established, mostly Christian refugees. While the latter recognized a common bond between themselves and the former, the longer-staying refugees also saw the new arrivals as dirty, uneducated, and "simple." Above all, they considered that the newly arrived women in their relatively revealing traditional clothes were inappropriately and immorally dressed. It became clear that these sorts of attitudes were significantly compromising not only the ease with which the new arrivals were able to fit into the existing refugee population but also the effectiveness of healthcare programs. One young woman whose baby was acutely ill with dysentery was told by a Karenni health worker with whom she saw at the camp clinic that it was her fault her baby was so ill, because the mother was dirty. This greatly upset her, so that when her baby's health deteriorated, she refused to return to the clinic. This and similar instances identified in the anthropologist's report led directly to a concerted effort by IRC staff and Karenni health workers to increase their sensitivity to these issues. Similarly, the data showed that the new arrivals' attitudes to health education conducted by Karenni CHEs were such that they found the information amusing at best and irrelevant at worst. This was utilized by the IRC staff and CHEs to refine the health education program's objectives and approaches. In particular, the staff encouraged Karenni CHEs to make program messages interesting and relevant, as well as to explain why the behavior change was desirable.

When not being a formal part of IRC may have helped the flexibility of the research agenda, it also perhaps lessened the impact of the findings on agency staff. Furthermore, the researcher's breadth of focus did not necessarily facilitate the presentation of results to the relief agency. A few staff members viewed some of the information felt by the anthropologist to be important context as extraneous and irrelevant. Indeed, in trying to overcome the skepticism of some staff, general conclusions were deliberately overstated stressing "dire" consequences to programmatic outcomes if attention to culture was ignored.

Another issue that compromised the reception of the field research concerned the fact that the "answers" to some of IRC's prior questions were not as expected. In particular, the new arrivals claimed neither to have specialist traditional health practitioners, such as midwives, nor to have widespread knowledge of plant medicines and other nonmagical curative techniques. In general, illness was perceived as being caused by the disturbance or theft by evil spirits of the victim's "soul," and cured by appropriate magical rituals aimed at restoring the soul. Yet this contradicted the prior belief of some relief workers that the community had both specialist midwives and plant medicines. As far as plant medicines were concerned, the information collected concerned only personal remedies; research indicated both that these remedies were not widespread and that they were always secondary to the principal, magical curative techniques. In the case of specialist midwives, there seemed to be a subtle misunderstanding of the nature of "specialist," so that individual older women experienced in assisting childbirth had been mistakenly thought of by some NGO staff as being people whose "job" it was to provide a midwifery service.

The anthropologist perceived the methodology of the research and the presentation of the results as problematic. The collection of data is often difficult in complex humanitarian emergencies and, as a result of various constraints, may not always be fully accurate. The rapidity with which these events unfold, the nature of international responses to them and the various challenges found in these situations all compound the problem (see Williams and Bloland this bulletin). In the Karenni emergency of 1996, IRC asked for a rapid ethnographic assessment (see Williams this bulletin). Although this was useful for describing an overview of the situation, a longer period of participant observation would have blended data from interviews with those from actual observed practices, thus strengthening some conclusions. Other constraints included a lack of fluency in the new arrivals' language (they cannot speak Burmese) which meant that the anthropologist had to rely on interpreters from the longer staying refugee community to conduct interviews. Furthermore, although attempts were made to be sensitive to issues of gender, other factors such as class and religious differences between the interpreters and the new arrivals may have further confounded the data collected.

Conclusion

War, famine, civil conflicts, and political persecution continue to result in mass displacement of populations. The disruption of known social systems can have devastating effects on families, communities and even entire cultures.

The impact of the displacement experience on Karenni people and their culture is greatly influenced by the interactions, both positive and negative, among the refugee population itself, the host country and NGO workers providing assistance. These influences both helped and hindered the adjustment experience of incoming Karenni refugees.

A high degree of cultural awareness and sensitivity on the part of NGO staff make the experience of accessing health care, receiving food and supplies and rebuilding the community less foreign, less traumatic, and more feasible. Cultural sensitivity on the part of aid workers is not only ethically desirable, it is imperative. IRC attempted to impart this sensitivity on its field workers by utilizing an annual retreat to train the aid workers, incorporation of local staff into the health delivery teams, use of expatriate Burmese staff, and, finally, recruitment of a social scientist to conduct ethnographic research. NGOs are not responsible for the feelings and mental attitudes of their staff or existing refugees. Nevertheless, in the context of health and illness, they can greatly influence the attitudes and behaviors of the displaced, in addition to local and expatriate health care workers whom they support.

Since the inception of IRC's work with the Karenni, the organization attempted to avoid aid dependency through a low profile intervention effort, a policy to work with the community and ethnic political infrastructure and refugee capacity building. This included attempts at better understanding the Karenni culture. IRC expatriate staff longevity in the posts working with the Karenni was two to three times longer than any other NGO working with ethnic Burmese. This allowed the staff and refugees to build trust and understanding. Still, there were numerous assumptions made by IRC staff as to who were, and were not, Karenni and what beliefs systems they operated under.

The IRC primarily worked with a relatively elite level, coordinating with the KNPP leadership and drawing Karenni health workers from a Christian, comparatively well educated, group of refugees. To an extent, in this as in other situations, this elite bias was unavoidable. Nonetheless, attempts can be made to expand the social levels on which in-depth refugee/NGO contact is made.

Furthermore, the Karenni situation amply demonstrates the need to be aware that refugees in key liaison positions—such as the Karenni health workers—are not necessarily representative and fully understanding of the overall displaced population. Similarly, outsiders with an apparent closeness to the situation—such as the Burmese relief workers—may sometimes be too close and sometimes too distant to broker culture effectively. The role of social scientists, too, is often problematic. The methodological constraints in a complex emergency situation are great and researchers available on the ground, or with knowledge of a given ethnic group, are not necessarily those with previous experience working with relief NGOs. Nonetheless, all three categories can play a useful role in the mediation and/or translation of culture for the achievement of greater understanding between NGOs and refugees and the improved effectiveness of health-care programs.

Social scientists need awareness of the difference in language between public health and social science disciplines and should strive to present data in terms that recognize these differences. In particular, the data need to be concise and directly linked to specific improvements in the delivery of public health interventions. With the time constraints of frequently stressed and overworked NGO relief workers, efforts should be made to make recommendations as practical and feasible as possible given the complexity of these emergencies. Likewise, relief agencies should be clear in their need for tightly focused research that can be utilized by program planning and implementation.

Although cultural brokers in the form of refugee health staff, expatriate native country staff returning to assist or other bilingual workers may be useful in developing culturally appropriate relief programs, they do not have the training and skills of a social scientist. While most NGOs would not implement health interventions without a medical team nor establish water and sanitation programs without water engineers, many continue to field teams in foreign environments with little training in cross-cultural sensitivity. The headquarters of NGOs need to recognize that their staff has little formal cross-cultural education and thus, they need to create innovative training programs to cover this deficit. Some agencies do offer brief training prior to field placement or in-country seminars during placement but rarely is there time or funding, for example, to conduct language training—IRC was a notable exception to this. Other possibilities include the inclusion of a social scientist in the headquarters' staff who can assess the appropriateness of programmatic planning and implement cross-cultural training. It is time for relief agencies to ensure that alongside initial rapid epidemiologic assessments, ethnographic assessments occur, thus enabling a culturally comprehensive approach to public health interventions in complex humanitarian emergencies.

Cultural sensitivity includes awareness not only of traditional beliefs and practices concerning health and illness, but also, for example, familiarity with who plays what roles within traditional social structure. If such understandings exist, relief programs can be directed through culturally appropriate social channels. Only in this way are short and long-term objectives likely to be achieved.

Notes

Disclaimer. The views expressed within this chapter are solely those of the authors and do not reflect those of the United States Public Health Service or the United States Department of Health and Human Services.

Acknowledgments. The authors would like to acknowledge the current and former staff of the International Rescue Committee–Thailand, including Yuzana Khin, who provided countless insights into the development of this manuscript. Most importantly, we wish to thank the Karenni people for the opportunity to work alongside them during these difficult times.

1. A refugee is classified as "a person who owing to a well founded fear of being persecuted for reasons of race, religion, nationality, membership in a particular social group, or political opinion is outside of the country of his nationality" (United Nations 1951:57).

2. Internally displaced persons have been uprooted from their homes because of war, civil strife, persecution, and famine but have not crossed international borders (International Committee of the Red Cross 1998).

3. For more information on the plight of the Karenni and other ethnic groups from Burma, the reader is referred to Boucaud and Boucaud 1992, and Smith 1991, 1994, which contain detailed analyses.

4. The camp where most of the new refugees were settled was officially open to IRC staff only. While not having any "formal" relationship with IRC in the camp, the "informal" status with the agency allowed the anthropologist access to this closed area.

References Cited

Burma Border Consortium
    N.d. Monthly Reports to the Committee for Coordination of Services to Displaced Persons in Thailand. Unpublished data.
Boucaud, Andre, and Louis Boucaud
    1992 Burma's Golden Triangle: On the Trail of the Opium Warlords. Bangkok: Asia Books.
Clinton-Davis, L., and Y. Fassil
    1992 Health and Social Problems of Refugees. Social Science in Medicine 35(4): 507–513.
Dennis, Philip A.
    1994 The Life of a Cultural Broker. Human Organization 53(3):303–308.
Demusz, Kerry
    1998 From Relief to Development: Negotiating the Continuum on the Thai-Burmese Border. Journal of Refugee Studies 11(3):231–244.
Dudley, Sandra
    1997 Recent Arrivals in Karenni Camp #2: An Ethnographic Report. Unpublished data.
International Committee of the Red Cross
    1998 Guiding Principles on Internal Displacement. International Review of the Red Cross 324:545–556.
Smith, Martin
    1991 Burma: Insurgency and the Politics of Ethnicity. London: Zed Books.
    1994 Ethnic Groups in Burma: Development, Democracy and Human Rights. London: Anti-Slavery International.
Toole, Michael J., and Ronald J. Waldman
    1990 Prevention of Excess Mortality in Refugee and Displaced Populations in Developing Countries. Journal of the American Medical Association 263(24):3296–3302.
    1993 Refugees and Displaced Persons. War, Hunger, and Public Health. Journal of the American Medical Association 270(5):600–605.
United Nations
    1951 Convention Relating to the Status of Refugees. In Twenty-Five Human Rights Documents. Center for the Study of Human Rights, ed. Pp. 57–67. New York: Columbia University.
U.S. Committee for Refugees
    2000 World Refugee Survey 2000. Washington, DC: U.S. Committee for Refugees.
Woodrow, Peter J.
    1998 Promotion of Health Care among Khmer Refugees in Greenhill Site B. In Rising from the Ashes: Development Strategies in Times of Disaster. Mary B. Anderson and Peter J. Woodrow, eds. Pp. 301–314. London: Lynne Riener Publishers.

CHAPTER 5

A Practical Discussion of Applied Public Health Research in
the Context of Complex Emergencies: Examples from
Malaria Control in Refugee Camps

Holly Ann Williams
Peter B. Bloland
Malaria Epidemiology Branch, Division of Parasitic Diseases, National
Center for Infectious Diseases, Centers for Disease Control and Prevention

Complex emergencies, including refugees and internally displaced
persons, present massive challenges requiring coordinated humanitarian
efforts.[1] Although important public health research questions can be identified early in such situations, rarely is there opportunity to conduct applied
research during the beginning phases of a complex emergency due to the
competing demands of meeting essential needs. Funding at this stage
must be directed toward establishing a secure environment for those displaced, as well as toward reducing the high levels of morbidity and mortality that frequently occur as a result of factors experienced before or during
the flight (e.g., famine, physical and/or psychological illnesses/injuries,
lack of shelter, feelings of fear and vulnerability, and distrust of officials).
The various nongovernmental organizations (NGO) that provide essential
services to the displaced population need to quickly establish their modes
of operation: cooperation must develop among the host country, the
United Nations High Commissioner for Refugees (UNHCR), the World
Health Organization (WHO), and among the NGOs themselves.[2]
    During this initial period, information gained from rapid assessments
of public health problems would be useful to agencies trying to allocate
scarce resources. Complementing the epidemiologic approach, rapid
community assessments that clearly identify the social structure, perceived
immediate needs and local expertise within the displaced population
would add valuable information to programmatic decisions. Data gleaned
from these assessments could identify community leaders, describe the
refugees' perceptions of their most pressing concerns and assist with setting
up participatory programs that, in the long run, could empower refugees

and help diminish their sense of powerlessness so often seen. However, because of the urgency of the initial period and the general chaotic nature of these situations, researchers are often viewed as an unwelcome intrusion during the time when NGOs and UNHCR are attempting to establish refugee operations. As the complex emergency situation lengthens and moves into a postemergency phase, the need for research, particularly in the form of intervention and evaluation studies, becomes more apparent and relief agencies are generally more willing to collaborate with outside researchers. Recently, albeit slowly, a call for research and monitoring and evaluation to improve the practice of humanitarian assistance has begun to be voiced (McClelland et al. 2000; WHO/ Federation for International Cooperation of Health Services and Systems Research Centers [FICOSSER] 2000). Research could provide baseline demographic and socioeconomic data, behavioral information concerning disease prevention and health promotion, identification of negative effects of relief programs, analysis of the cost-effectiveness of alternative interventions and other data important to areas of applied public health research.

This article offers examples from malaria control research because malaria is a pressing public health problem in many emergency situations, both those caused by conflict as well as by natural disasters. Each year there are an estimated 300–500 million clinical cases of malaria worldwide and, depending on the epidemiologic conditions, health and social consequences from malaria can be quite severe, particularly in sub-Saharan Africa. All regions of sub-Saharan Africa have seen significant refugee movements in the past five years, with recent notable examples including Burundi, Rwanda, the Democratic Republic of Congo, Sudan, and Sierra Leone. As of December 31, 1999, refugees and asylum seekers totaled 3,147,000 in Africa (U.S. Committee for Refugees 2000:2). Providing cost-effective malaria control for these displaced populations is a major concern of humanitarian agencies (see Figure 1).

Listed by the WHO as probable precipitating causes of the most severe malaria problems are migration, environmental disruption for agricultural or economic reasons, and sociopolitical unrest (WHO 1996). Malaria epidemics have been associated with population displacement caused by wars or natural disasters, particularly if heavy rains follow the natural disaster. Factors associated with the increased risk of malaria infection include: famine, lack of access to health care facilities, physical weakness, concurrent illness, low socioeconomic status, movements from nonmalarial areas to malarial areas, refugee settlement in high-risk areas, crowding with inadequate sanitation, and substandard housing. As these factors are features of displaced populations, it is easy to see the vulnerability of such populations to malaria (Bloland and Williams n.d.; Nájera et al. 1998).

A multidisciplinary approach is best suited to address the types of public health problems and questions associated with malaria control in complex emergencies. In order to provide appropriate diagnosis and

Distribution of Malaria

Refugee/Internally Displaced Populations

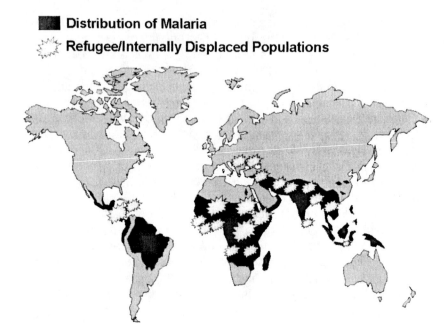

Graph compiled from data collected by UNHCR

Figure 1

treatment of malaria, outsiders must first understand the cultural background and local context from which people fled, for example: previous residential and travel histories, prior exposure and level of immunity to malaria, local understandings of febrile illnesses and how those understandings include malaria, acceptance of antimalarial drugs, use of personal protective measures (e.g., use of insecticide-treated materials and protective clothing, and limiting exposure outdoors during the evening or night), treatment seeking behaviors, and use of traditional prevention and healing strategies. Medical anthropologists can use these data to assist epidemiologists and public health practitioners to better understand factors that influence morbidity and mortality rates.

This chapter describes a practical approach to conducting research with displaced populations, focusing mostly on refugees in camps. It offers a stepwise approach to planning the research, identifies some of the potential obstacles in conducting such research and offers concrete suggestions for how to maximize the likelihood of having a research idea accepted by the agencies responsible for displaced populations. If these agencies are involved in the planning and implementation of applied research from the beginning, and if the research asks questions that may answer problems they have, there is a better chance of having the research findings utilized in programmatic decisions. This discussion focuses on factors that influence whether research will be accepted, as well as the implications for how research findings can be adapted for programmatic needs. Specific examples, both from published articles and personal experience, will be offered as illustrations from field research performed both in refugee camps and with self-settled populations. This chapter is particularly geared toward applied researchers and graduate students who would like to collaborate with relief agencies in conducting research for the benefit of improving the health of refugees in a camp setting.

The Research Process from Conceptualization to Dissemination of Results

Initial Steps in Gaining Approval

There are a few general guidelines to keep in mind when considering conducting research with displaced populations. Whenever possible, research should address problems identified as priorities by field staff or the host government, and the issues need to be relevant from a practical standpoint. The researcher should clarify and describe the magnitude of the problem both in quantitative and qualitative terms, work in concert with NGO partners or the government to identify feasible interventions, and use the findings to develop specific recommendations.

Although theoretically based studies have merit, the focus of such research needs to quickly attract the attention of humanitarian agencies. This is often a very different orientation for most academicians. The researchers should ask: "Why would an agency with limited resources [time, personnel, and finances] and competing demands want to participate in our research? Will the research findings address larger issues that gather the attention of others outside of the particular setting in which we wish to conduct the research? Are we willing to take the time to carefully craft a research proposal and the later research findings into language acceptable and usable to personnel in the field?" If these issues are addressed during each step of the process, the research will be more attractive to the agencies involved in refugee care and the findings will be more readily usable to address programmatic needs.

For anthropologists who attempt to work independently in situations of displacement, particularly with self-settled refugees, approval may be much harder to gain and a variety of creative strategies may need to be employed. One anthropologist attempted to return several years later to study a refugee settlement project in an area in Zambia where he had previously studied self-settled refugees, which resulted in several publications (Hansen 1979a, 1979b). Knowing the levels of bureaucracy he faced, while still in the U.S. he first requested permission from the New York office of the United Nations High Commissioner for Refugees (UNHCR), including with his request copies of his curriculum vitae and his publications in this area. He followed the requests with a personal visit to the New York UNCHR office, obtaining a formal letter of permission from this office, which the New York office also faxed to the Geneva office. From NY he flew to the Geneva headquarters of UNCHR, where he repeated the process of offering them copies of his past publications and curriculum vitae and requested their permission. He also showed them the approval letter from the New York office. These steps resulted in receiving permission from the Geneva office, granted in a formal letter, which they faxed to their capital office in Lusaka. Upon his arrival in Lusaka, he produced the UNCHR letters and, once again, repeated the strategy with the country-level office of UNHCR and permission was granted. However, the lead NGO agency refused him permission to enter. It was only by arriving from the capital in an official UNHCR vehicle and having proper documentation from various levels of UNHCR that the NGO finally accepted the legitimacy of his reason to enter the camp.

A more creative approach was needed several years later when Hansen and one of the authors of this chapter (Williams) attempted to return to the same area to continue a long-term study of the same refugees. Clearance was obtained at national levels. Part of this clearance involved meeting with and getting written permission from a Deputy Minister for Home Affairs, the office that granted permission for this type of study. This official also happened to be the son of the president at that time. As a matter of public relations, a photograph was taken of the president's son and the research team when they received his permission to work in the border area. After traveling two days to the field site, the research team was refused access to the border by the Provincial Governor, who cited security concerns. Hansen, as Principal Investigator, spoke for the team and showed all the "official" documents that granted permission. It was only when the photograph of the team with the president's son was produced that the Governor changed his mind and granted immediate entry to the area. This was an unconventional approach, but one that worked.

Recently, another anthropologist (Sommers in press) struggled to gain Tanzanian government permission to study refugees in an official rural settlement. He was denied access from the government, which has hosted refugees for many years. However, Sommers persisted and finally obtained official permission to study the few officially recognized refugees residing in the capital of Tanzania, Dar es Salaam. The approach he used was to rely on a Tanzanian colleague who was well placed in the government to represent his case and exert continued pressure for the necessary clearance. Having research clearance for the capital, he expanded his focus and discovered many self-settled urban refugees. His research resulted in one of the more innovative works in refugee studies, examining institutionalized fear and suspicion and urban social networks of self-settled refugees, an area that had been almost untapped before his research (see also Kuhlman 1995).

Generating the Research Questions

There are several approaches to generating public health research questions in the context of a refugee camp. First, questions can be generated from theoretical perspectives that have not been tested in displaced populations. For example, the acceptability and sustainability of insecticide-impregnated mosquito nets have generally been tested with stable communities. While the efficacy of the nets in stable populations is apparent (Aikins et al. 1998; Brieger et al. 1996; Habluetzel et al. 1997), there remain several questions as to how the nets could be used in a displaced population. For example: Is there a good way to hang a net with the plastic sheeting that is often distributed by UNHCR for initial shelter? Would refugees sell and/or trade the nets to gain commodities that might be more acceptable than what they receive in their basic rations package?

Another way to identify appropriate research questions is to review official reports from a series of complex emergencies and ask what patterns exist in the problems encountered while trying to provide humanitarian assistance. Technical reports written by NGOs, as well as monthly situation reports by UNHCR, are invaluable in understanding the day-to-day complexities of providing care to a displaced population. In addition, UNHCR and agencies responsible for providing health care to refugees produce monthly disease surveillance reports that show trends in illness patterns.

Epidemiologists and medical anthropologists can combine efforts aimed at diminishing the burden of disease. For example, drug resistance to antimalarials is a severe problem in sub-Saharan Africa, where many refugee situations exist. Testing the efficacy of antimalarial drugs can be combined with a qualitative study to determine refugees' acceptance of new antimalarial treatments. Social science research can also focus on treatment seeking behaviors to describe how and when refugees seek health care and their acceptance of and compliance with treatment. When done early in an emergency, such information could be vital in developing practical and effective treatment guidelines. Reports from surveys done in refugee camps in Goma, Zaire (now known as the Democratic Republic of Congo), indicated that most deaths did not occur in health care facilities (Centers for Disease Control and Prevention 1996; Goma Epidemiology Group 1995). Certainly there was a multitude of factors that influenced this situation, and the scope of the Goma crisis was larger than had been seen in many other refugee settings. However, in more manageable emergencies, social scientists and epidemiologists working together with NGOs providing health services could conduct rapid qualitative assessments to help identify obstacles to receiving care and could devise more appropriate solutions.

In addition to defining the scope of inquiry, it is important to carefully determine which phase of a complex emergency is most suitable for the type of research question you wish to ask. There are several ways to increase the feasibility of research in the initial phases of the emergency. It must have a narrow focus and a fairly simple design; a camp census may not yet be available during times of refugee influx, making complex sampling difficult. It should require a minimum of logistical support and not interfere with the routine provision of services as NGO partners may not yet have their full complement of staff or supplies, and the focus at this point is provision of immediate services. Also, it should be able to produce data that can be quickly analyzed and integrated into programmatic decisions regarding allocation of resources. Some public health problems can be addressed from the beginning by thoughtful camp design, which takes into account house construction (including what is feasible in the situation considering time and money, as well as the types of shelter common to the homeland of the displaced population), sanitation, and drainage and health care accessibility.

For example, during the first phase of a complex emergency, epidemiologists may do rapid assessments of the malaria situation with host and refugee populations to better anticipate the potential scope of the malaria problem. Depending on the scope of the emergency, this may be very limited. One of the authors (Bloland) participated in a rapid assessment of the population in Goma, Zaire, to obtain information on treatment seeking behavior and acceptability of drugs, as a rapid decision needed to have been made regarding which drugs were most appropriate for treatment of malaria in this situation. Because of the chaos at the start of the crisis, a carefully designed study would have been impossible to conduct, and the best that could be done was data collection of a superficial nature. In situations that are not quite as overwhelming as Goma, multidisciplinary teams can be fielded to gather data in a more organized and thoughtful manner. Entomologists may be needed to work with the epidemiologists to determine rapidly the most appropriate vector control strategies. Social scientists can work alongside these scientists to gather information concerning refugee perceptions about housing needs: What are the typical houses that a particular group ultimately plans to build within the camp? Do the refugees envision having livestock near their homes? Will they prefer to have homes located near standing water? Although refugees often are not given a choice in their living arrangements, understanding how and why refugees make decisions regarding their lifestyles might explain later patterns of behavior that have implications for broader, long-term malaria control strategies and other public health concerns.

Other research questions are best suited for the postemergency situations, where the displaced population has a stable living arrangement, community leaders have been identified, and logistics are made routine. An example for this period of time is an evaluation of the use of health care facilities provided by the NGOs, including a description of the gaps in service and the use of ancillary services such as traditional healers.

Stable refugee situations that last many years, such as those found in the Thai border areas, have provided an opportunity for research field stations in the surrounding communities to gather epidemiologic and behavioral trends that can be followed over a longer period. For example, data could be gathered about patterns in drug resistance or in refugees' use of malaria control interventions. An excellent example of this research comes from the Thai/Myanmar border, where the Shoklo Malaria Research Unit has studied antimalarial drug resistance in Karen refugees (Dolan et al. 1993; Lindsay et al. 1998; Luxemburger 1996; Price et al. 1996).

Another example is the research done by the NGO HealthNet International with Pakistani and Afghan refugee populations in conjunction with various in-country malaria control programs (Bouma and Rowland 1995; HealthNet International 1998; Hewitt et al. 1994; Rowland 1999; Shah et al. 1997). Recognizing the constraints of using insecticide-treated nets in complex emergency situations, including cost, unsuitability for sleeping areas in tents or under plastic sheeting, importation difficulties, etc., the NGO applied insecticide to the traditional Muslim wrap called a *chaddar*. This approach was culturally acceptable and demonstrated, for a displaced population, a creative alternative that provided appropriate and effective prevention against malaria.

In addition to improving the quality of life for the refugees themselves, research findings from these relatively stable populations have enhanced understandings about the development and use of personal protection and vector control strategies, as well as information about multidrug resistance to antimalarial drugs and clinical problems (Rowland 1998). These findings have been widely used by the malaria community and have applicability for use outside of displaced populations.

However, long-term situations may not be suitable for research questions for which one is trying to understand differences between the refugee population and the host population, particularly if the camps are open and refugees freely mix with the host population. As a result of humanitarian efforts, the refugee population might have access to better health care than the host population. The more stable the refugee population is, the more likely it will begin to resemble the host population in terms of disease and disease risk.

Regardless of the phase in which the research is planned, if the proposal addresses questions that might be generalized to other displaced populations, or if the findings can have a direct impact on refugee services, the better the likelihood of acceptance from NGOs and UNHCR.[3]

Establishing Collaborative Partnerships

Once the purpose of the research and the phase of the emergency most suited for the research are defined, a venue for the research must be identified. The location of the camp involves not only picking a specific country, but may also involve knowing the specific features of each camp within a country, should that country be host to multiple sites for refugees. This decision may be influenced by factors such as: (1) security (is the camp housing refugees who are a security risk, such as combatants, and will UNHCR and the host country allow you in the camp?); (2) road and/or flight access into the refugee area (if housing arrangements for refugee staff are located outside of the camp, is daily travel to the camp available, particularly during the rainy season?); (3) availability of housing and vehicles for a research team (often in small rural areas surrounding refugee camps, particularly in the initial emergency phase, all housing is occupied by agency staff); (4) size and stability of the camp (is the camp population stable or is there tremendous influx and movement in/out of the camp? Is an adequate sample size feasible?); and (5) willingness of the particular NGOs within that camp to approve and facilitate the research.

Once a site is chosen, developing collaborative relationships with all key players involved in the refugee situation is crucial to having the research accepted. It is important to understand the length of time needed to obtain research approvals, as well as the time needed to establish collaborative relationships with the various agencies involved in providing services to the displaced population. First, all relevant ministries within the host country need to be alerted to the research, and need to give approval. This may include both the Ministry of Health and a Ministry of Home Affairs (or whatever ministry manages the regulation of the refugee population, perhaps through a Commission for Refugee Affairs). In addition to obtaining approval from the offices in the capital city, most ministries have regional or provincial and district level offices that also require visits from the research team. In each situation, once given approval to conduct the research, you would need to carry with you duplicate copies of any official documents supporting the research so all agencies involved could receive their own copies of the approvals. Gaining such approvals may require a field trip specifically designed for this purpose in advance of initiating the study. It is often useful to assume that such a preliminary trip is needed so that these costs can be written into the budget in advance.

Contact must also be made with UNHCR and/or WHO, depending on whether the situation involves refugees or internally displaced persons.[4] UNHCR often has a main base of operations in the capital city of the host country, but it is essential to also meet the staff from field and subfield offices. As UNHCR is mandated to protect the rights of refugees, program representatives and officers need to clearly understand the scope of the research and how/when/where the research will be conducted.[5] If working with NGO partners for the research, it is useful to have letters of introduction from each agency that clearly spell out the collaborative partnership and the support that you will receive from each respective agency.

Last, but not least, close relationships need to be developed with the NGOs that work within the camp setting. Each agency probably will have a specific mandate for the types of services that they will be providing and, thus, a research project may overlap with several agencies. Each involved agency should clearly understand and agree to its own role in the research. In our experience, we have found that it is important to introduce the researchers to representatives from all agencies within a camp setting so that they are cognizant of research efforts conducted within the camp. This serves the researcher well when additional information is required about camp services that are not directly provided by the NGO with which the research team has a partnership. One should keep in mind that important, established contacts might be needed for future research projects. We held informational meetings with representatives of all NGOs involved in camp operations, both at the regional and district level. Once clearance was gained and prior to the start of collecting data, we also held briefings in the camp setting with camp managers and section leaders and all community health care workers so that information about our research could be dispersed throughout the camp. This helped to clarify the true purpose of our involvement with the refugees. In addition, it allowed the refugee leaders to voice their concerns about the effect of malaria on adults and to ask questions about why adults were not being included in our particular study. It gave us an opportunity to explain how malaria can be prevented and treated.

Ethical Review

If the research comes from either an academic or a federally or state-funded institution, it is necessary to submit a proposal and gain approval from the institution's Institutional Review Board (IRB).[6] If the applied researcher is from another type of institution, this step may or may not be necessary. Depending on the volume of proposals that the IRB must review, this step might take several months. If research is planned during an acute phase of an emergency, there may be provisions for such limited time frames and the researcher should check with his or her own institution for ways to expedite the review. In addition to the ethical review in the United States, it will likely be necessary to complete an ethical review in the host country as well. For public health research, most ethical reviews are the responsibility of the Ministry of Health within each country. However, it is necessary to learn which suboffice handles such requests and whether there are multiple layers of approval that are necessary. For example, in Malaŵi, ethical approval is granted by the Ministry of Health. In other countries, such as Kenya, Mozambique, Tanzania, and Zambia, additional institutions within the Ministry of Health or other independent institutions or ad hoc committees have the responsibility for overseeing all health related research. In some situations, the research institutions may have several bureaucratic levels of clearance. In addition to knowing a realistic time frame for gaining clearance, it is important to ask what fees are associated with such approvals so that the costs can be included in research budgets.

There are clearly ethical concerns particular to refugee populations that are outside the scope of this paper. For example, research questions that focus on issues pertinent to both the refugee population and the surrounding communities have to be justified if the research addresses only the refugee population. In situations such as this, it is vital that the ministry of health within the host community be involved in the early stages of the planned research.

Conducting the Research

Travel Logistics

Once the site has been selected and all approvals have been obtained or are in process, attention must be given to the logistics of getting staff and supplies to the site.[7] Depending on the situation, office supplies, workspace, and photocopying capacity may be sorely limited. It is wise to check with your primary NGO partner to determine whether any of these services exist, and whether there is a fee associated with their use. In advance of the trip, duplicating printed research material (i.e., informed consent letters, interview guides, and laboratory data forms) in the United States is less expensive than having to do this work in many overseas areas. However, this cost must be balanced against the costs of added freight, particularly if the material will be sent as excess baggage on a flight. Air freight is generally cheaper but may add on additional time. In any event, it is necessary to learn about customs restrictions at the port of entry. If no one from the research team will be available at the port of entry when the goods are expected to arrive, it is helpful to have someone from the partner NGO be present to explain the shipment at customs. Whether the supplies are shipped in advance or carried by the research team, an inventory of supplies should be available for the customs officers with the intent of use clearly stated on an attached letter of introduction. For our research projects, we clearly list which supplies must return to the United States (such as microscopes and other expensive equipment) and which remaining supplies will be donated to the host country and the NGOs. A letter of support from the NGO should also be included with the introduction letter and inventory sheet. Before our trips we worked closely with the home office of our NGO partner in the United States to determine all restrictions regarding custom clearance and associated fees. These advance planning strategies made it possible for smooth clearance of supplies for three associated projects over a four-month period.

Consideration must be given to moving supplies to the field site. Again, advance planning will ease the start of the research project. Determine the most advantageous way to move supplies to the site. If air transportation is involved, check with the NGO partner to determine how often flights are canceled and factor in additional time for such cancellations. If small charter flights are necessary to reach the site, determine the cost of such flights and amount of weight that can be carried on each flight. UNHCR graciously allowed us to send personnel and supplies on their UN planes, but we had to comply with a strict weight limit. Thus, we had to allow several extra days for all supplies to reach our site. As has been demonstrated over and over in the area of emergency food provision, transport and distribution of supplies can also be blocked by extraneous factors, such as military or political obstructions (Seaman 1999).

Hiring of Local Staff

Often a research team needs local assistance with a project, particularly if team members are not conversant with the local language. Employment opportunities that can be offered to regional or district level staff are generally appreciated by the host country. In addition, hiring opportunities can be seen as building capacity for the ministry of health, particularly if the research question has relevance for the local population. When requesting assistance with staff, it is useful to be able to detail what training will be done with the staff and how that can complement or enhance training offered by the Ministry of Health. When hiring host country personnel, it is necessary to find out if staff can be seconded from their positions. With this type of arrangement, the project would cover only cost of travel and per diem for the time spent in the field. Some countries have a set allowance that covers any work or travel outside the person's regularly scheduled duties.

If at all possible, consideration should also be given to hiring refugee personnel, particularly if the research will involve going into the refugee community as opposed to being solely based in the health care facilities. However, payment of staff becomes a politically sensitive issue when using both host country and refugee personnel. The salaries for nationals are generally much higher than the salaries allowed for refugees, which are usually established by each specific NGO or based on an interagency pay scale that must be followed. As well, UNHCR should also be included in the discussions about hiring refugee staff. It is important to remember that NGOs operate within limited budgets and the fee schedule established by the research team should match what the NGO considers proper for that particular situation. NGOs have been in the unfortunate situation of having outside researchers hire refugee staff at salary levels that the NGO cannot support for future projects after the researcher leaves. This often creates tension between the research staff and the NGOs, and makes it more difficult for future researchers to hire locally.

Security Issues

Depending on each situation, security issues are an important consideration for most research teams as they do not have the infrastructure that NGOs and UNHCR staff have in place. A courtesy visit to the research team's embassy (or consulate office if an embassy is not located in the country) in the capital city should occur before leaving for the camp. When arranging such a visit, ask to speak with the particular officer who is in charge of refugee affairs for the embassy. Also, it can be arranged to leave a photocopy of the first page of a passport with the security office, which is useful if one encounters difficulties in the field, loses one's passport or are robbed. Often the refugee officer will have updated reports about the general camp situation, which might be useful in understanding the relationships within the camp setting.

Meeting with the embassy staff also offers an opportunity to provide a briefing about the work that you intend to do. These talks offer the embassy personnel additional insights as to specific problems or concerns regarding the refugee population and, often, the researcher can extrapolate the research question to larger issues that are facing the host country. In addition, a talk provides an opportunity for the researcher to highlight the activities of his or her home institution and describe the types of projects in which the institution is involved. Again, this is another way to foster relationships for future work. During our preliminary site visits, we met with embassy staff, as well as staff from the United States Agency for International Development (USAID). In addition to our briefing meetings, we provided informal lectures to the embassy personnel and their families on how to prevent and treat malaria. This was well received and appreciated, and established for us an excellent working relationship with the diplomatic community.

Security issues do not end with entrance into the camp. It is advisable to discuss the logistics of travel back and forth to the camp with the NGO partner so that the research team is aware of any travel restrictions that might be in place. For example: Are vehicles available for weekends if the NGO staff normally do not work on weekends? If the research team cannot stay in the refugee camp or settlement area, what time must the research team leave in the evening? Are there any curfews in effect? It is essential that all members of the research team meet at least once with the camp director, as well as visit the UNHCR office within the camp, prior to initiating any activities in the camp.

In addition, communication among UNHCR, the NGO partner, and the research team is crucial. The research team needs to know if any special events are happening in the camp that might affect a working schedule, or if there are threats to security. Depending on the location of the camp, border camps might be particularly vulnerable to disruptions from the outside. It is worthwhile for the research team to inquire whether they will have access to any two-way radio communications, either from handheld radio units or from a vehicle unit. During our research, UNHCR provided us with vehicles that allowed us to have radio contact with all NGOs and the base operations for UNHCR. This proved to be very useful when we were trying to contact camp leaders and UNHCR representatives, as well as for maintaining contact with team members who were working in various areas of a large camp.

Communication with refugee leaders is essential for success of any research project. As mentioned previously, refugee leaders need to be involved in the planning and acceptance of any research project in order to assist in recruiting refugee participants, particularly if the research involves any invasive procedure such as drawing blood (especially with children). Researchers need to remember that displaced populations have been traumatized in a variety of ways, and often are distrustful of outsiders whose roles in the camps are not clearly seen. Just as in any applied research settings, particularly overseas fieldwork, having the support of community leaders provides an easier access to the population of interest. If the research team is going to have access to the residential areas of the camp, section leaders need to be informed in advance so that community meetings can be held to explain why strangers are visiting the housing areas. Particularly in longer established camps, newcomers are noticed and can attract large crowds when walking around the camps. If the research team wants to conduct individual or focus group interviews, this can be disruptive. As well, the large crowds can be seen as an added security risk from the perspective of the camp managers. Camp leaders and managers will appreciate attempts to minimize these types of situations.

Placing the Research in the Context of the Local Situation

Given the burden that most refugee situations place on the host country, political sensitivity to the needs of the host country is important. In terms of public health, the impact of refugees on the burden of disease locally may occur in different ways. Refugees may introduce different or resistant forms of diseases that occur normally in the host population, diseases that were eradicated from the host population or diseases unknown to the host population. Socially, the impact of refugees may influence the availability of jobs, increase the cost of food or alter what commodities are locally available. If refugees migrate from the camp or settlement areas into the surrounding communities (e.g., for labor migration or to trade in local markets), it may be difficult to maintain national control programs, such as for malaria or tuberculosis. Environmentally, inadequate camp sanitation may pollute water sources used by local communities, deplete sources of firewood, and threaten natural resources (Dick 1985).

Most often, countries that have inadequate internal resources to meet their own needs host displaced populations in the developing world. The health care system of the host country is often woefully inadequate to cover the needs of its own citizens, and donor assistance is vital to improving the health status of the country. Compounding the problem are the examples listed above that may have detrimental effects on the host population. In addition, the level of training of health care professionals in local communities is often inadequate for the demands of refugee situation. In some host countries, laboratory and surgical assistance is sought from district and regional health care facilities, or the host country provides care to refugees residing outside of camp areas (Porignon et al. 1985). When an influx of refugees arrives, humanitarian assistance brings with it an array of health and sanitation services that are absent from the surrounding local communities. Yet, often, public health training is focused on rapidly creating a cadre of trained health care workers from within the refugee population, but this training is not offered to local health care personnel.

This can be a very sensitive situation when trying to conduct research with the refugee population, particularly if the research involves interventions that might improve the refugee situation while not providing a direct benefit to the host population. For example, mosquito nets are clearly seen as an important malaria control strategy. If the refugees are supplied with nets, the host country might rightly ask about the provision of such nets for local residents who also lack protection. Another example would be providing intermittent malaria prophylaxis to pregnant refugee women when this service is not provided in district health care centers.

Although researchers are not in a position to offer donor assistance and rarely have enough money to conduct research in multiple sites (i.e., the refugee camp and the surrounding local community), consideration should be given to how the study results could be used to benefit the local communities. If feasible, attention should be directed toward strengthening the capacity of the host ministry of health in providing services to the displaced and host populations. This can occur through hiring or seconding local health care workers as staff for the research, offering to give in service lectures to the local staff, or donating equipment that remains at the end of the project. As well, the contributions of the host personnel should be recognized publicly at the end of the study (Porignon et al. 1995).

The research questions should be scrutinized to determine whether the questions pertain solely to the refugee population or whether there are broader public health implications for the host community. If the research is seen as a component of a larger, long-term project, it is more attractive to the host country if the project results can be applied to developing sustainable projects that would benefit both the displaced and the host populations. Certainly, issues involving malaria control are important to both populations, but other public health research can also be expanded to include the local community, such as nutritional interventions, sanitation strategies, or understanding treatment seeking behaviors. Our results from antimalarial drug efficacy trials in a refugee camp gave important information about levels of drug resistance that complemented drug efficacy studies done locally by the Ministry of Health. Together, these data are now being used to determine the most effective antimalarial treatment policy for the host country as well as for the refugee population. In addition, the relationships made with donor agencies and NGOs in the initial stages of the project allowed us to offer input into programmatic decisions about the allocation of funds and resources for future projects planned to address the problems of malaria control, both in the displaced and the host population.

Dissemination of Results

The Value of Briefings and Debriefings

The final stage of any research project is the dissemination of results. Regular briefings during the course of the research offer an opportunity for the researcher to discuss with the NGO partners the direction of the findings as well as to make any needed modifications in the research, particularly with qualitative projects. At the end of the project, debriefings must be scheduled to discuss the findings and how they might be applied programmatically. For many field projects, final analysis and writing will not occur until the researchers return home. However, preliminary analysis can usually begin at the site, and social scientists have long valued the input of key informants through the analysis phase. While final reports are not written for several months at the end of most projects, oral debriefings are extremely valuable for a variety of reasons. Although mentioning the need for debriefings might seem trite to experienced researchers, often researchers on their first applied field trip might not see the importance of the time spent in this activity. When time and money are limited, as often happens at the end of research projects, the need for spending time in many meetings seems to lose importance.

Scheduling debriefings with all levels of personnel—from camp staff, to district and regional offices, to ministry-level personnel—allows the involved individuals to continue contributing to the project. In addition to answering questions that arise during the course of the research, different perspectives are discussed that could enhance both the theoretical and applied interpretation of the results. As humanitarian agencies have a service orientation with an emphasis on the need to quickly disseminate information and new interventions, it is crucial that they have a sense of the data gathered in the research. A debriefing allows the agency representatives and the researchers to determine the most useful application of the findings. In addition, a discussion of programmatic needs will highlight additional areas of research that are needed.

A word of caution is necessary when a project requires significant analysis after completion of field activities. It is important that everyone in the debriefing understands that the data are preliminary and subject to modifications and, therefore, should not be disseminated. Clearly state in large, bold letters on the top of preliminary documents left behind that data in the report are not for quotation or citation. Providing the field staff with an expected date of completion often helps them in planning.

Conclusion

Significant public health research questions can be addressed during all phases of complex emergencies involving displaced persons. However, because of the complexities of such situations, careful thought must be given to each step of the design and implementation of the research. Research that answers questions from both theoretical and applied perspectives often has relevance for addressing public health concerns in other areas. Multidisciplinary teams, such as social and behavioral scientists and public health practitioners, when working in concert with NGOs that provide health services, can translate research findings into usable programmatic applications.

Notes

Disclaimer. The views expressed within this chapter are solely those of the authors and do not reflect those of the United States Public Health Service.

1. See Chapter 2 of this bulletin for the most widely accepted definition of refugee. In addition, the Organization for African Unity also includes "every person who, owing to external aggression, occupation, foreign domination or events seriously disturbing public order in either part or the whole of his country of origin or nationality, is compelled to leave place of habitual residence in order to seek refuge in another place outside his country or origin or nationality" (Organization of African Unity 1969). Asylum seeker refers to persons who arrive in a host country (without prior identification as a refugee) and, on arrival, request asylum. They are awaiting a refugee status determination (U.S. Committee for Refugees 2000).

2. Overall responsibility for internally displaced persons, such as those in Sudan, usually rests with the World Health Organization or UNICEF (United Nations Children's Fund) and not with UNHCR.

3. Pressing questions remain about how to best provide preventive and curative health services in refugee settings, particularly in emergency situations, such as Goma, where the size and movements of the displaced population overwhelmed agencies' abilities to initially provide adequate services to the entire population. Studies in these situations will provide data that directly benefit refugee groups, yet might not be translatable to the general population.

4. In some situations, UNICEF may be the leading agency (see note 2).

5. While UNHCR has the mandate to protect the rights of refugees as defined by international refugee law, the rights granted to refugees differ from those of internally displaced persons. However, ethical considerations and security issues are pertinent to internally displaced persons, and it is necessary to develop similar collaborative relationships with WHO and all agencies managing internally displaced persons. For further discussion of the difference between refugees and internally displaced persons, refer to Barutciski 1998.

6. Within the past year, WHO, UNHCR, and other agencies have established a committee specifically designed to offer technical and ethical review of research planned with displaced populations.

7. Throughout the stages of conducting research with refugee populations, it is critical that the researcher maintain flexibility. Refugee situations, particularly in the initial stages, can change quickly. Populations can shift with unexpected influxes of new refugees, governments can forcibly repatriate refugees without advanced warning and apparently stable border situations can erupt with fighting, all of which may directly influence, if not prevent or preclude, planned research activities.

8. The authors wish to acknowledge the assistance of Drs. Art Hansen, Brad Woodruff, Brent Burkholder, and Kay Tomeshek in the preparation of this chapter.

References Cited

Aikins, Moses Kweku, Julia Fox-Rushby, Umberto D'Alessandro, Patricia Langerock, Kabir Cham, Laura New, Steve Bennett, Brian Greenwood, and Anne Mills
   1998 The Gambian National Impregnated Bednet Programme: Costs, Consequences and Net Cost-Effectiveness. Social Science and Medicine 46:181–191.
Barutciski, Michael
   1998 Tensions Between the Refugee Concept and the IDP Debate. Forced Migration Review December 1998:11–14.
Bloland, Peter B., and Holly Ann Williams
   N.d. Malaria Control During Mass Population Movements and Natural Disasters: Review and Recommendations. Unpublished MS.
Bouma, Menno, and Mark Rowland
   1995 Failure of Passive Zooprphylaxis: Cattle Ownership in Pakistan is Associated with a Higher Prevalence of Malaria. Transactions of the Royal Society of Tropical Medicine and Hygiene 89:351–353.
Brieger, William R., A. E. Onyido, John D. Sexton, Venatius I. Ezike, Joel G. Breman, and O. J. Ekanem
   1996 Monitoring Community Response to Malaria Control Using Insecticide-Impregnated Bednets, Curtains and Residual Spray at Nsukka, Nigeria. Health Education Research 11(2):133–145.
Centers for Disease Control and Prevention
   1996 Morbidity and Mortality Surveillance in Rwandan Refugees: Burundi and Zaire, 1994. Morbidity and Mortality Weekly Review February 9:104–107.
Dick, Bruce
   1985 The Impact of Refugees on the Health Status and Health Services of Host Communities: Compounding Bad with Worse? Disasters 9:259–269.
Dolan, G., Feiko O. ter Kuile, V. Jacoutot, N. J. White, C. Luxemburger, L. Malankirii, T. Chongsuphajaisiddhi, and F. Nosten
   1993 Bednets for the Prevention of Malaria and Anaemia in Pregnancy. Transactions of the Royal Society of Tropical Medicine and Hygiene 87:620–626.
Goma Epidemiology Group
   1995 Public Health Impact of Rwandan Refugee Crisis: What Happened in Goma, Zaire, in July, 1994. Lancet 345:339–344.
Habluetzel, A., D. A. Diallo, F. Esposito, L. Lamizana, F. Pagnoni, C. Lengeler, C. Traore, and S. N. Cousens
   1997 Do Insecticide-Treated Curtains Reduce All-Cause Child Mortality in Burkina Faso? Tropical Medicine and International Health 2(9):855–862.
Hansen, Art
   1979a Managing Refugees: Zambia's Response to Angolan Refugees 1966–1977. Disasters 3:375–380.
   1979b Once the Running Stops: Assimilation of Angolan Refugees into Zambian Border Villages. Disasters 3:369–374.
HealthNet International
   1998 HealthNet International Annual Report 1997. London: HealthNet International.
Hewitt, Sean, Muhammad Kamal, Nasir Muhammad, and Mark Rowland
   1994 An Entomological Investigation of the Likely Impact of Cattle Ownership on Malaria in an Afghan Refugee Camp in the North West Frontier Province of Pakistan. Medical and Veterinary Entomology 8:160–164.
Kuhlman, Thomas
   1995 Asylum or Aid? The Economic Integration of Ethiopian and Eritrean Refugees in the Sudan. Research Series No. 2. Leiden: African Studies Center.
Lindsay, S. W., J. A. Ewald, Y. Samung, C. Apiwathnasorn, and Francois Nosten
   1998 Thanaka and Deet Mixture as a Mosquito Repellent for Use by Karen Women. Medical and Veterinary Entomology 12:295–301.

Luxemburger, C., K. L. Thwai, N. J. White, H. K. Webster, D. E. Kyle, L. Maelankirri,
T. Chongsuphajaisiddhi, and F. Nosten
    1996   The Epidemiology of Malaria in a Karen Population on the Western Border of Thai-
    land. Transactions of the Royal Society of Tropical Medicine and Hygiene 90:105–111.
McClelland, Donald G., with Elizabeth Adelsko, Richard Hill, John Mason, and Robert Muscat
    2000   Complex Humanitarian Emergencies and USAID's Humanitarian Response.
    USAID Program and Operations Assessment Report No. 27. Washington, DC: Center
    for Development Information and Evaluation/USAID.
Nájera, Jose A., R. L. Kouznetzsov, and Charles Delacollette
    1998 Malaria Epidemics: Detection and Control. Forecasting and Prevention. WHO/MAL/
    98.1084. Geneva: World Health Organization.
Organization of African Unity
    1969   Convention Concerning the Specific Aspects of Refugee Problems in Africa. Addis
    Ababa: Organization of African Unity.
Porignon, Denis, Jean–Pierre Noterman, Phillipe Hennart, René Tonglet, Etienne Mugisho
Soron'Gane, and Tarcisse Elongo Lokombe
    1995   The Role of Zairian Health Services in the Rwandan Refugee Crisis. Disasters
    19:356–360.
Price, R. N., Francois Nosten, C. Luxemburger, Feiko O. ter Kuile, L. Paiphun,
T. Chongsuphajaisiddhi, and Nicholas J. White.
    1996   Effects of Artemisinin Derivatives on Malaria Transmissibility. Lancet 347:1654–1658.
Rowland, Mark
    1998   Review of Published Literature on Malaria Control in Complex Emergencies. Re-
    port for the Expert Group Meeting on Malaria Control in Complex Emergencies, WHO
    Roll Back Malaria/Division of Emergency and Humanitarian Action, Geneva, December
    1–2, 1998.
    1999   Permethrin-Treated Chaddars and Top-Sheets: Appropriate Technology for Pro-
    tection against Malaria in Afghanistan and Other Complex Emergencies. Transactions
    of the Royal Society of Tropical Medicine and Hygiene 93:465–472.
Seaman, John
    1999   Malnutrition in Emergencies: How Can We Do Better and Where Do the Responsi-
    bilities Lie? Disasters 23:306–315.
Shah, I., Mark Rowland, P. Mehmood, C. Mujahid, and F. Razique
    1997   Chloroquine Resistance in Pakistan and the Upsurge of Falciparum Malaria in
    Pakistani and Afghan Refugee Populations. Annals of Tropical Medicine and Parasitol-
    ogy 91(6):591–602.
Sommers, Marc
    In press   Fear in Bongoland: Burundi Refugees in Urban Tanzania. New York: Berghahn
    Books, Inc.
U.S. Committee for Refugees
    2000   World Refugee Survey 2000. Washington, DC: U.S. Committee for Refugees.
World Health Organization
    1996   World Malaria Situation in 1993, Part 1. Weekly Epidemiological Review 71:17–22.
World Health Organization/Federation for International Cooperation of Health Services and
Systems Research Centers
    2000   Use of Health Economics for Decision-Making in Complex Emergenices. Report of
    a WHO/FICOSSER Meeting, Paris, December 16–18. Cahiers Sociologie et de
    Démographie Médicales 40:159–188.

CHAPTER 6

Public Health in Complex Emergencies: Toward a More Integrated Science

Ronald Waldman
Program on Forced Migration and Health, The Joseph L. Mailman
School of Public Health, Columbia University

Holly Ann Williams
Malaria Epidemiology Branch, Division of Parasitic Diseases, National
Center for Infectious Diseases, Centers for Disease Control and Prevention

The provision of health services for refugees and internally displaced persons during complex emergencies has become an increasingly frequent activity in international health over the past 20 years. Though perhaps not yet a science, a discipline of refugee health has emerged. However, documentation of successful public health interventions is lacking.

The literature is scanty—a recently issued inventory of health research in emergencies is a thin volume (World Health Organization [WHO] 1999). For the most part, lessons have not been learned from clinical trials or epidemiological and anthropological observational studies, and a base of applied research for complex emergencies does not exist (Burkle 1999). Instead, summaries of personal and/or organizational experiences, often termed *best practices* have been the most important sources, and these are generally found in the "gray" literature—the files and reports of government agencies or nongovernmental organizations (NGO). Some of the "published" literature in refugee studies, as well, draws upon personal experience and impressions (Cromwell 1988).

Best practices, however, are not necessarily good practices. In this article, we review some of the priority activities that have become more or less accepted as common procedure in emergency settings and their aftermath. We will review situations where their implementation is appropriate, and where there is reason to question. We touch on four technical areas with which most emergency workers are familiar: (1) establishing population size for both epidemiological and supply purposes, (2) food distribution and consumption patterns, (3) water supply and use, and (4) the delivery of health services.

We suggest areas where social science research can complement epidemiological assessments in order to provide technically sound and operationally feasible guidance to NGOs, United Nations agencies, donors, host countries, and, of course, to the refugees themselves. The goal of improving current practice is to decrease the time needed to reduce the risk of excess morbidity and mortality to manageable levels. Much of the literature and "best practices" are summarized in three principal sources, which will be used as the basis for this discussion (Centers for Disease Control and Prevention 1992; Médecins Sans Frontières 1997; Sphere Project 2000).

Addressing Crucial Areas of Emergency Response

Population Determinations

Estimation of the Magnitude of the Emergency. Although exceptions are becoming frequent, it has been generally accepted that the magnitude of an emergency can be measured in terms of its impact on mortality rates in the affected population.[1] Yet, for many years, even this basic epidemiological and demographic parameter was not routinely measured and recorded, as it was difficult in the midst of an emergency to obtain an objective, quantifiable assessment of whether the situation was improving or worsening.

The importance of establishing mortality rates at the outset of an epidemic should be self-evident. Mortality is a very specific indicator of the health status of a population. If it is markedly elevated, the need for a health sector response is clear. The urgency of the situation, the level of resources required, and the kinds of health services that must be provided are dependent on the rate at which the population is dying. Whether or not the response is adequate can be determined by seeing in which direction and at what speed mortality trends are moving.

Two major factors are involved in determining an accurate and representative mortality experience of a population: (1) the number of deaths and (2) the size of the population. It has been learned repeatedly that relying on reports of death from health facilities or from camp or local officials is a mistake.

Only active surveillance, where deaths are counted as they occur or as bodies are buried, can provide accurate information. Graveyards, for example, should be visited daily to ensure an up-to-date count of deaths.

It is essential to know the size of the population (denominator) to be able to establish crude and age-, gender-, location-, and/or disease-specific mortality rates at regular intervals and to follow their evolution. For epidemiological purposes, the best way to establish accurate denominators would be through ongoing registration of the refugee or displaced population.

It would be important to establish registration early and to pay meticulous attention to maintaining as complete and timely a system of enumeration as possible. Of course, registration is easiest when the target population is sheltered in camps. If it is dispersed among the host population, figures are "guesstimates," at best. As populations in emergencies are highly dynamic and their size can change dramatically in short periods of time, merely counting deaths (numerator data) can give a very inaccurate picture of overall health status. For example, in late March and early April 1999, following the bombing of Yugoslavia by NATO forces, an estimated 700,000–800,000 refugees fled Kosovo for Macedonia and Albania. By July, they were gone from both the camps and the local households in which they had temporarily settled. Conducting epidemiological surveys to determine mortality and causes of morbidity in this population was fraught with seemingly insurmountable problems (Physicians for Human Rights 1999).

Calculating rates from inaccurate population estimates can be more misleading than having no denominators at all. Various methods for estimating population size have been tried. Technologically advanced methods, such as satellite imagery, have not always been useful because of their inability to detect dwellings under cloud or forest cover. Hand-held geographic information systems that count dwelling units and combine them with an estimate of the number of inhabitants per dwelling have also proven unsatisfactory at times because those without shelter (the most at-risk), are missed.

Household surveys have substantial value, but can be wildly inaccurate because of difficulties in establishing a sampling frame, because people are not distributed homogeneously throughout the area and because the homeless are missed. For these reasons, best estimates of the population of refugees in Goma, in what was then Zaire and is now the Democratic Republic of Congo, in July 1994 ranged from 500,000–800,000, a range far too wide to provide estimates of mortality rates with any reasonable degree of confidence. An even more egregious example of inaccurate counting may be the estimates of the number of deaths suffered by the Cambodian population at the hands of Pol Pot and the Khmer Rouge in the 1970s and 1980s (Heuveline 1998).

To Be Counted or To Remain Unseen: Behavioral Factors Influencing Population Estimates. The real problems in establishing the size of populations are not methodological. Instead, they stem from the fact that while epidemiologists find it essential to have accurate denominators in order to inform health policies, the intended beneficiaries often feel that it is essential to avoid being counted. Individuals who have fled a repressive government are often highly distrustful of any official-looking written documents or systems of registration. This sentiment can be easily understood—by definition, refugees have fled out of fear for their lives.

Sometimes, because registration systems are often used to calculate the quantities required of both food and essential non-food commodities such as tents, plastic sheeting, and jerry cans, the opposite situation prevails. Instead of trying to avoid being counted, refugees try to be counted as many times as possible. By doing so, they try to get relief authorities to overestimate the number of people in need in the hope that at least adequate quantities of potentially life-saving supplies will be available. This tendency to manipulate assistance systems though inaccurate reporting of numbers is a normal response to dire circumstances and should not be interpreted, as it sometimes is, as a sign of moral deficiency. In either case, by seeking to avoid being counted, or by trying to be overcounted, refugees can make life difficult for epidemiologists.

Community Involvement

Eliciting support from key members of the displaced community may make the task of the epidemiologist easier. When trying to either register displaced persons or obtain accurate mortality counts, it is essential that community members be involved. It is incumbent on those who need the data to take whatever measures are necessary to explain why those data are needed and to enlist the cooperation of the community in obtaining the data, even though the process may frustrate well-meaning epidemiologists (Harrell-Bond et al. 1992). Understanding the social structure of the displaced population will assist in identifying the most appropriate community leaders from whom endorsement and assistance should be sought. With the shifts in social organization that occur with displacement, ethnographic techniques should be used to identify the lines of community-level power and influence on a formal and informal level. Community elders, reacting to the stress of displacement, may no longer function in the role of community leaders and younger members may be assuming social roles traditionally not afforded them (Médecins Sans Frontières 1997). If the need for cooperation is put into terms that explain the benefits of being counted, such as the need to accurately order food and medicines, community cooperation may be more forthcoming. In the past, relief workers have resorted to extreme measures to try to ensure accurate counts of refugees. Examples include forcing people to march like cattle through corral-like structures and marking refugees with semipermanent dyes, such as gentian violet, to avoid double counting. One of us (RW) has even heard it suggested (but not by an epidemiologist) that refugees should be tattooed with their registration number! The problem is, to paraphrase Harrell-Bond, that epidemiologists have "taken it for granted that [their] interest in ensuring survival is sufficient to legitimize [their methods]" (Harrell-Bond et al. 1992).

Relying on community members to conduct active surveillance for mortality data has been shown to yield very good information. For example, mortality rates were high in northern Iraq when Kurds fled to the mountainous region on the Turkish border in fear of reprisals by the Saddam Hussein government following its defeat in the Gulf War of 1991. To measure deaths, graveyard workers were contracted to keep accurate counts and to report to health authorities. In other situations, especially in emergencies affecting Moslem populations, religious leaders have been given traditional burial shrouds to distribute to the families of the dead to allow fulfillment of the burial ritual in accordance with traditional practice. The number of shrouds dispensed was recorded and reported. In eastern Zaire, an area in which a large number of refugees "settled" after fleeing Rwanda after the genocide of 1994, an epidemic of cholera of unprecedented magnitude occurred in the first weeks of the emergency. It has been reliably estimated that more than 45,000 people died during the course of the epidemic, yet fewer than 5,000 of those deaths were reported by the established health care system. The other deaths were counted by teams of volunteers who picked up corpses from the roadsides where survivors had carried them for transport to mass gravesites (Goma Epidemiology Group 1995).[2] When burial procedures are less well organized, such as when families carry their own dead to secluded burial sites in the bush at an undetermined distance from settlements, community informants can be engaged as part of the active surveillance teams. In the midst of the most traumatic emergency, the best information is not obtained through a health system established primarily by expatriate relief personnel. Instead, it should be obtained by understanding community practices and engaging the assistance of influential community members.

Food Distribution and Consumption Patterns

Caloric Needs of the Displaced—Political or Biological? After estimating the magnitude of the emergency, the international relief community must provide what is required to sustain life. The quantity of food required is essentially determined by the size of the population. The role of other factors, such as climate, age, and sex structure of the population and levels of activity, is detailed in the existing recommendations, but tends to be accorded only a secondary level of importance. Unfortunately, there have been instances when even after refugees have become dependent on international aid, the provision of inadequate quantities of food has been associated with sustained high mortality rates for a protracted period. The most notorious of these episodes may be the experience of Hartisheik A Camp, in eastern Ethiopia, in 1988–89, when mortality rates continued to increase for nine months after the opening of the camp (Centers for Disease Control and Prevention 1990).

The minimum "standard" of food provision for refugees has been changed a number of times since 1980. Initially established at 1,500 Kilocalories (Kcal) per person per day, this standard was raised to 1,900 and then to 2,100 Kcal/person/day (World Food Programme and United Nations High Commissioner for Refugees 1997). The biological needs of refugees and displaced persons have not changed during this time, so it is difficult to explain why there has been so much difficulty establishing food requirements. They should be the same as those for all other human beings.

Control of Resources. It is also somewhat difficult to explain why international authorities believe they should exercise absolute control over donated food after it has been distributed. The problem is, admittedly, a delicate one. It is clear that in some circumstances food distribution processes, if not adequately controlled, can contribute to a war effort. The distribution of food to Interahamwe forces in refugee camps in eastern Zaire in 1994 and the expropriation of food by armed militia in southern Sudan are two oft-cited examples. In situations like these, needy people can be deprived of their due and, as a result, their nutritional status can be impaired. The paradox of humanitarian assistance contributing to the proliferation of conflict poses important ethical problems to the international community.[3]

However, excessive control of the food distribution process can also work to the detriment of the health status of the recipient population. In Somalia in 1980, the United States Agency for International Development (USAID) donated much of the food that was distributed to refugees. A team of USAID officials, sighting sacks with the trademark "shaking hands" emblem being sold in the marketplace, threatened to suspend food aid on the assumption that refugees were selling excess food for cash. The assumption was mistaken. It was the bags themselves, not the food, that were being sold—the refugees had transferred the grain to other containers and were selling the equally valuable burlap. Why should not refugees be given the "privilege" of deciding for themselves how to use whatever resources might be available to them? Wilson (1992) notes that the erroneous concept of refugees as dependent and passive recipients fails to take into account creative strategies for providing food for themselves. Recognizing refugees' existing livelihood and food acquisition strategies and acknowledging their ability to meet their own needs would go a long way in improving nutritional support.

A better-documented example of the potentially negative impact of excessive donor control is drawn from Uvira, Zaire, in 1996 (Reed and Habicht 1998). When representatives of the World Food Programme (WFP) found donated food being sold in local markets, they reduced the ration being distributed to refugees, assuming that refugees were consuming what they needed and selling the surplus. This study, however, found that refugees were selling the WFP rations to obtain foods that were more palatable, diverse, and nutritious. In fact, of all the purchases made by the refugees with money they raised from selling donated food, 85 percent were for other food. It is interesting that one-fourth of the sales of food aid would not have occurred if salt had been included in the distributed rations. On the basis of their findings, the authors concluded that merely meeting energy requirements is not sufficient: "neglect of cultural preference, micronutrient needs, and cooking practices can seriously reduce energy intake" (Reed and Habicht 1998:130).

Disastrous Consequences from Lack of Knowledge of Cultural Practices. Of even greater interest than the quantity of food delivered to meet the energy requirements of refugees should be a discussion of the quality of their diet. Although current guidelines call for 10–12 percent of the total energy content of the diet of the target population to be provided as protein and 17 percent as fat, these targets have proven elusive. Even more difficult to achieve has been ensuring an adequate micronutrient intake through fresh or fortified foods.

The importance of the micronutrient content of the diet became dramatically clear in 1981 in Somalia (Magan et al. 1983). Clinicians in a number of remote camps for refugees fleeing the Ogaden war in Ethiopia reported a syndrome consisting of joint pain and swelling, limb tenderness, and pain upon walking, particularly noticeable in children just beginning to walk. After a number of weeks, radiographic images of some of the patients were sent abroad where, eventually, the diagnosis of scurvy (Vitamin C deficiency) was made. In retrospect, it was determined that the major source of Vitamin C in the nomadic refugees' normal diet had been camel's milk. Deprived of their livestock, the entire refugee population became dependent upon the small quantities of Vitamin C that were available to them from onions and tomatoes they were able to purchase in the local markets to which they had limited access. Shortly after those markets were closed by political decree, symptoms of scurvy began to appear. When Vitamin C supplements were provided to the population, the outbreak quickly subsided. It is not surprising that the diagnosis was not made earlier; scurvy had not existed as a public health problem since the Irish potato famine of the 19th century.

What is quite surprising is that outbreaks of scurvy have continued to occur in populations dependent upon external food aid (Desenclos et al. 1989). By 1989, multiple outbreaks of scurvy had been documented throughout the Horn of Africa, and the prevalence was found to be as high as 25 percent in some camp settings, always increasing as a function of the time people had resided in the camps. Tellingly, outbreaks occurred after three to four months of consuming relief food that was almost totally deficient in Vitamin C.

The failure of the international community to have learned a lesson in regard to scurvy is compounded by the repeated occurrence of pellagra in refugee populations. In 1989 and 1990, outbreaks affecting more than 18,000 people occurred in refugee camps for Mozambican refugees in Malawi (Malfait et al. 1993). Pellagra is a vitamin deficiency disease caused by inadequate consumption of foods containing niacin, one of the B-complex vitamins. The major characteristics of pellagra are a rash on sun-exposed parts of the body, diarrhea that can be severe, changes in mental status and death. In the past, pellagra had been highly prevalent in the southeastern part of the United States, southern Europe, southern Africa, and other parts of the world where maize is the staple cereal. However, these outbreaks in the Mozambican refugee camps were the largest reported anywhere in the world since World War II. In this instance, the cause of the outbreaks was attributed primarily to a lack of access to groundnuts, which are high in niacin content and are a staple in the diet of the region. Neither locally available groundnuts nor any other niacin-containing food were included in the rations provided to the refugees by the international community.

As with scurvy, pellagra recurred. The international relief community does not seem to be able to take the necessary steps to provide essential dietary requirements to those populations that are entirely dependent upon donated food. As this article is being written, pellagra is occurring in other conflict-torn parts of Africa to which the World Food Programme is providing rations (Baquet et al. 2000). Many other instances of micronutrient deficiency have been documented, including iron-deficiency anemia, Vitamin A deficiency (xerophthalmia) and Vitamin B_1 deficiency (beriberi).

Promoting Self-Determination. Designing better strategies for promoting self-determination in food-aid recipients should be a primary consideration in implementing food distribution programs. Suggested ways of doing this all have one theme in common—refugees must be allowed to be more in charge. Decisions concerning humanitarian assistance need to be demand driven and derived from the perceived and actual needs of the target population, not supply driven as a function of what the international community wants to, or can, provide. For example, cereals are considered an important food in the West and are often the largest component of food aid. However, for them to be edible and palatable, wheat and other cereals must be prepared and cooked. As Landman (1999) notes, obstacles to using cereal foods include the need for fuel, utensils, potable water, insufficient information about recipes and the lack of other, complementary ingredients. All these obstacles are common in complex emergencies. Appropriate food aid can only be delivered when it is based on knowledge of consumer habits, food preferences, and culturally ingrained cooking practices.

Understanding the Root Causes of Malnutrition. The role of social scientists in ensuring adequate nutrition for refugees should be apparent. The process of food procurement, transport, and distribution is slow, often taking months. There is time to undertake a thorough study of how to provide a fully adequate ration covering population needs for energy and micronutrients in a way that minimizes human dependence and preserves dignity. Anthropologists can also team with epidemiologists to do community surveys using anthropometric methods to evaluate the success of nutritional interventions.

While knowledge of local food preferences, production and supply is necessary to effectively plan programmatic interventions designed to alleviate malnutrition, it is often not enough. The concept of vulnerability as a social concept and its relationship to malnutrition is not well understood, as some individuals are better able than others to mitigate factors commonly associated with malnutrition (Jaspars and Shoham 1999; Webb and Harinarayan 1999). Vulnerability can be viewed as a function of both hazard and coping strategies. Individual perceptions of risks and potential actions based on previous experience, community-level responses and realistic appraisals of what can be done to mitigate the situation are all examples of factors that play a role in determining the effectiveness of coping strategies (Webb and Harinarayan 1999).

Using a population-based model that seeks to go beyond the narrow focus of clinical malnutrition and its outcomes, the Public Nutrition approach uses a multidisciplinary perspective to analyze the root causes of malnutrition, including social, political and economic determinants (Borrel and Salama 1999; Landman 1999; Young 1999). In addition to understanding the causes of malnutrition, an assessment is made of both available resources and constraints that influence actions within specific contexts including power structures, public policy, advocacy, poverty levels, household food security, social and care environments, status and rights, conflict resolution, and access to health care. Community participation and involvement is stressed in all levels, from the point of programmatic design through all aspects of project cycles including monitoring and evaluation. Considering the areas of research and advocacy to which anthropologists have long contributed (as described in Chapter 1—areas such as household economics, food security, livelihood assessments, policy development, etc.), social scientists can contribute actively to project teams that employ a Public Nutrition approach. Although this model specifically addresses nutrition, the need for the broader context-specific orientation is important in addressing other public health concerns.

In a short essay distributed by United Nations High Commissioner for Refugees (UNHCR), the United Nations Administrative Coordinating Committee/Subcommittee on Nutrition summarizes much of the above discussion by presenting four common myths surrounding refugees and food (Mason et al. 1992):

1. *Starving people can eat anything.* Starving people will not eat anything nor will they be necessarily grateful to receive it. Suppliers of relief food should work closely with social scientists to determine the real, not externally perceived, needs of the concerned population. What should be delivered is culturally preferred, palatable

food offered in adequate diversity in a form that can be easily prepared according to custom.

2. *Refugees can manage with one standardized, less than normal,
   per capita ration.* In fact, energy requirements need to be com-
   mensurate with the biological needs of the population, taking into
   account its demographic composition, activity levels, climate, and
   other pertinent factors, and not dependent on "negotiated settlements" of the donor community.

3. *Trading (or selling) foods is unacceptable.* The fact that refugees
   trade some foods is no grounds whatsoever for reducing the
   amount of food made available. In most cases, refugees improve
   their lot by trade, barter, or sale of whatever resources they have,
   some of which might very well be in the form of food aid.

4. *Energy adequacy equals ration adequacy.* Recurrent outbreaks of
   micronutrient deficiency diseases in populations dependent on
   externally provided rations, resulting in high rates of morbidity and
   mortality, are a severe indictment of the international relief community.

Sanitation and Water

In addition to food (and shelter), consideration must be given immedi-
ately upon the onset of an emergency to two life-saving necessities of displaced populations: (1) sanitation, especially the disposal of liquid and
solid human waste and (2) the quantity and the quality of water available
for consumption.

The Need for Community Involvement in Sanitation. Sanitation can be a
particularly thorny problem, especially where large numbers of people are
forced to live in a relatively confined space. One of the easiest methods for
dealing with the disposal of feces in the early stages of an emergency, at
least in sunny, hot and dry conditions, is the demarcation of certain areas
as "defecation fields." Although the notion of communal, outdoor defecation is not a pleasant one, and is almost always culturally inappropriate, in
an emergency this may be a measure that can contribute to the preserva-
tion of public health.

As soon as possible, however, latrines should be dug. In some instances, such as during the Balkans crisis in the spring of 1999, portable
toilets may be made available; however, they are expensive and comparatively difficult to maintain. In an early stage, it might be necessary to provide communal latrines. Latrines, however, require regular and careful
maintenance. Unless clear and specific responsibilities are assigned, communal latrines (one enclosed latrine or open trench per 50–100 people) are
frequently neglected. Family latrines are much more effectively main-
tained. Again, one of the most important elements is making sure that families and communities understand why latrines are important and why and

how they must be cared for. In all cases, ensuring the cultural appropriateness of waste disposal systems is the only way to ensure their success.

Without the full engagement of the community and appropriately designed assessment of cultural practices prior to embarking upon a latrine construction program, the results can be disastrous. An example of an expatriate program implemented without the requisite baseline investigations occurred in 1980 in Somalia, when a relief unit of the Swedish Army built high-quality latrines in a large refugee camp. In order to beat the oppressive heat, the expatriates worked in the early morning hours, with their backs to the rising sun. Following their construction of a large number of sturdily built latrines, the expatriates discovered, to their chagrin, that the population would not use the latrines—the refugees would not defecate when facing Mecca. All cultures have specific customs—and many taboos—regarding defecation and the disposal of fecal material. In order to ensure that refugees are treated with dignity and to preserve public health to the greatest degree possible, it is important, even in the early phases of an emergency, to work with the community and to take their cultural values into account.

The Politics of Water Supply and Distribution. Water is a precious commodity in an emergency setting. The current recommendation is that a minimum of 15 liters per person per day for all purposes be supplied. This amount is sometimes held to be "impractical" and, in the early phases, this standard can be lowered to as little as 5 liters per person per day. It is important to guard against the politicization of the water supply in emergencies. Public health officials must manage the water supply carefully and take special precautions to ensure that water distribution is as equitable as possible, for fear that some individuals or social groups might be deprived of even the barest minimum required for survival. To manage water most effectively, normal distribution and usage patterns should be investigated. The water collection process must be protected—access to water sources should be easy and safe. Water collection vessels of adequate volume, but which conform to customary practice, should be provided. Although it has been learned that narrow-necked containers are effective at protecting water from contamination by hands at the point of collection, their widespread adoption and consistent use should be ensured through health education interventions and not by decree.

Water Quality. The provision of sanitation facilities and an adequate amount of water are probably more important in the emergency phase, but the relief community must also pay attention to the quality of water provided.[4] There are many ways to disinfect water, but those that are simplest and quickest can be managed and implemented from within the community. The most common way of ensuring that water is clean is to add chlorine. However, there is a narrow line between the concentration of chlorine required for disinfection and that which can be easily tasted—and many people object strongly to even a hint of chlorine taste. Once again, engaging the community in dialogue and discussing the advantages and disadvantages of water chlorination in advance can be useful.

One clear advantage of chlorination is that it is simple. The addition of one or two drops of a dilute hypochlorite solution to a bucket of water works quickly and effectively. During the cholera epidemic in Goma, when women fetched water from Lake Kivu (the probable source of infection), it would have been possible to hire members of the community to stand by the shore of the lake with eyedroppers and to disinfect the water being carried back to the camps. Instead, more sophisticated solutions, involving the importation of high-technology water tankers were implemented, resulting in considerable delay before adequate quantities of clean water were available to most of the population. Again, reliance on external aid, insufficient study of the habits of the population, and lack of involvement of the community in implementing appropriate interventions may have contributed to the perpetuation of elevated mortality rates.

Provision and Use of Health Care Services

In the early phases of most complex emergencies, an important proportion of excess mortality is attributable to communicable diseases (Toole and Waldman 1990). Measles has been shown to be a particularly devastating killer in these situations—so much so that the organization and implementation of mass measles vaccine campaigns for all children aged six months to 12 years has become a reflexive activity. Diarrheal diseases have also been highly lethal, and these two conditions have been responsible in many settings for as much as 60–70 percent of all mortality. Malaria and pneumonia have been other consistent causes of death.

Excess mortality is to be expected in emergencies. In fact, as already mentioned, the existence of excess mortality helps define a situation as an emergency. Conditions are ideal for the rapid transmission of communicable diseases, and normal channels of access to and supply of health services have been seriously disrupted. Still, focusing the earliest activities of the relief effort on a few simple principles could probably help to minimize morbidity and mortality. As has been discussed above in regard to counting, food provision and water supply, the earliest and most earnest involvement of the community is crucial. Many relief workers in the health sector, thrust into a very stressful, chaotic situation for which they have received no specialized training, tend to fall back on ways that were successful for them in the past. They build clinics and hospitals, throw the doors open, and begin to diagnose and treat patients who come to them seeking care.

Focusing Health Care in the Right Direction. However, as the Goma, Zaire, (1994) experience taught so vividly, many people in emergencies do not seek health care from foreigners in clinics. Most deaths occur not in the hospital, but in the community. Based on these experiences and on a model developed for the prevention of childhood mortality in stable situations in developing countries but is applicable to emergency settings, priorities for health activities at the community level can be established (Waldman et al. 1996). For example, continuing breastfeeding and maintaining appropriate weaning practices will contribute greatly to survival. The international relief community must encourage these practices and discourage reliance on breast milk substitutes and supplementation of infant diets with inappropriate foods. This is especially true in emergencies, when the chance of food contamination is high and the ability to monitor food intake can be compromised.

This simple principle has been repeatedly violated, especially in the emergencies in northern Iraq in 1991 and in the Balkans in 1999. Essential early interventions would include learning about infant feeding practices in the affected population and accelerating health education efforts by enlisting influential community members in the effort. For example, training community-based health workers to visit households, providing health education during breastfeeding and weaning periods, and doing active surveillance for signs of malnutrition could contribute greatly to survival.

For many preventive actions, the affected population will always be at least partially dependent on external assistance. In addition to food, water supply, and latrine construction, humanitarian agencies also provide at least some of the knowledge, logistics ability, organizational skills, and material resources for vaccination programs and for access to condoms and other preventive aspects of reproductive health programs. Preventive health services, in other words, are very much a shared responsibility in emergencies, with both the providers of aid and its recipients being responsible for rapid and effective implementation.

On the curative side, a division of labor is even more important, and it is incumbent upon the relief community to understand that its efforts cannot be confined to the "health system." Fully equipped field hospitals have been built within days of the onset of an emergency, and highly sophisticated laboratories have been established. But these measures serve, at best, a minority of the population, usually those who are sheltered in close proximity.

It is crucial to recruit, train, and supervise members of the community to explain to people what services are available, where they can be found, who will be providing them and what people can do to maintain their health and to survive under abnormally adverse conditions. Sometimes, refugee populations will be relatively unfamiliar with the diseases that can affect them and their children. Scurvy and pellagra are classic examples, although these diseases were equally unfamiliar to the health professionals charged with providing care. The largely urban Kurdish population of northern Iraq was totally unprepared for the epidemic of cholera that broke out while they were living in pitched tents in the mountainous region on the border with Turkey. Refugees from malaria-free zones at high altitude in Africa are unprepared for epidemics of malaria, which occur when people are forcibly displaced to malaria-endemic areas. In these situations, where refugees are naïve about potential health risks, the international relief effort should warn them and carefully explain recommended treatments. When the health professionals are caught unaware, the need for the displaced communities and the relief workers to work together becomes even more crucial.

Treatment-Seeking Behaviors. When ill or injured, the displaced must decide whether they want to treat themselves or whether they should seek treatment outside the home or community. In an emergency, where health services can be minimal and professionally trained staff can be in short supply, it can be helpful to encourage home care, assisted or not by health workers drawn from the community. A review of the registers of health centers from many emergency settings has shown that minor conditions are sometimes overrepresented. Investigation often reveals that those most likely to consult at health centers are those who can. More severely ill individuals remain at home, unaware that health services are available, unwilling to or incapable of taking advantage of them. Even potentially life-threatening conditions such as childhood diarrhea, in their early stages, can be treated at home, even in emergency settings (Werner and Sanders 1997).

Empirical data that describe health-seeking behaviors during a complex emergency, for the most part, do not exist. Criteria used for determining treatment and the degree to which adherence to any recommended treatment occurs are usually not known. Informal systems of drug distribution and availability in a complex emergency have not been documented, which is worrisome in an age of increasing drug resistance. Almost nothing is known about how traditional systems of care are used. The numbers and types of healers available, when they are consulted and perceived etiologies of illnesses are important data to gather.

When people do decide to seek assistance from the established health services, it is essential that those responsible for providing health care do so competently. Yet, just as refugees can be unfamiliar with the diseases they might experience in a new setting, many expatriate health care professionals will be unfamiliar with the characteristics of the health conditions they will encounter in emergencies, and will be unprepared to treat these conditions appropriately. Few health workers in developed countries know how to rehydrate children with severe diarrhea or adults with cholera. Fewer still know that pneumonia in children can be accurately diagnosed clinically and presumptively treated without reliance on X-ray or antibiotic sensitivities. Expatriates have rarely, if ever, seen cases of cerebral malaria or become familiar with the treatment regimen for uncomplicated malaria. As mentioned above, expatriate knowledge of traditional healing is often woefully inadequate. NGOs should consider individual levels of knowledge in tropical diseases when hiring health care professionals, and offer brief training programs before the staff enters the field. Using field-experienced senior level staff to mentor junior staff could help new staff adjust to the realities of providing health care in complex emergency situations.

Both in southeast Asian and African refugee camps and during periods of resettlement in the United States, inexperienced practitioners often have mistaken traditional healing practices, such as burning or coining, as signs of abuse. Health professionals made critical negative judgments about the caregiving abilities of refugee families, while refugees were shocked and bewildered by the sometimes accusatory, hostile attitudes of the staff. Again, the need to have at least a cursory understanding of ethnic health practices and perceived illness etiologies is crucial for encouraging the affected communities to utilize relief health care services.[5]

Emergency relief has been largely an amateur enterprise, and young health professionals work long hours, for little pay and the turnover of expatriate health staff is rapid. It is not unusual for teams to arrive in an emergency with the intention of staying for three to four weeks. However, at least for the major NGOs, there is no excuse for claiming at this point that there is a lack of experience or skills in providing relief care (Zetter 1999). Recently, efforts have begun to raise the level of professionalism of health workers in emergencies; graduate programs are being developed in a number of schools of public health, and groups such as the International Committee of the Red Cross and several schools of public health are offering a series of short courses. UNHCR, WHO, and the Sphere Project (www.sphereproject.org) are currently developing manuals and guides. Some of the larger, more experienced NGOs, following the leadership of Médecins Sans Frontières, are developing specialized health units, encouraging longer contracts, and providing appropriate training to their personnel.

Yet, however competent the health services become, in the end the care of a patient almost always reverts to a caretaker in the community, either a mother, other family member or community health worker. Few people who arrive ill leave a health center well. Most return home during the recovery period. Most deaths occur in the home, not in the hospital. For this reason, what is said and the manner in which it is said is often as important as what is done to patients or their relatives during their relatively brief time of contact with the health center.

Giving instructions for follow-up to clinical care is difficult in the best of circumstances. One can easily understand how serious this problem becomes in the heat of an emergency, crowded health centers and transcultural settings, and where language difficulties abound. In addition, it is important to remember that patients who have recently been uprooted and have fled to unfamiliar surroundings for fear of their lives may be reluctant to entrust their health or that of their loved ones to foreigners. The only way to ensure a reasonable degree of compliance with drug prescriptions, recommendations regarding behavioral change and advice as to when to return for further care is to develop a comprehensive system of home follow-up as early as possible in the course of an emergency. Concentrating on providing health services within the community through a system of satellite clinics and health posts is a daunting undertaking. However, the slow rate at which morbidity and mortality have returned to baseline levels in many recent emergencies has been documented, and it seems fair to suggest that the careful implementation of peripheral services would result in a quicker return to more acceptable mortality levels. In addition, there have been many examples of overreliance on hospitals and clinics staffed primarily by expatriate personnel. These observations have led many experienced public health workers to conclude that health services in emergencies could be vastly improved by initially concentrating on providing care to the most peripheral levels of the community.[6]

A recent paper (Bhattacharyya and Murray 2000) describes the use of a participatory approach to community assessment and planning in Ethiopia. Community members and health staff jointly identified and prioritized health concerns and developed action plans using qualitative and quantitative approaches. While this was done in the context of a nonemergency setting, similar approaches could be tested in complex emergency situations.

Identifying the Most Vulnerable. Concentrating care in the communities would also assist public health practitioners in identifying and accessing vulnerable populations. Women and children have always been identified as the two most at-risk populations in complex emergencies, with less attention paid to other groups such as the elderly or the physically and/or mentally disabled. Understanding the social structure of a displaced community and addressing the political and social issues that underlie risk, such as the impact of poverty and/or impoverishment on health, are key elements in determining which specific groups have special needs or are at risk. In any programmatic planning or implementation, it is also essential that representatives of these vulnerable populations be involved to ensure that their interests are fully represented (Médecins Sans Frontières 1997).[7]

Broadening the "Lessons Learned"

Most of this chapter has concentrated on acute needs during the emergency phase of complex emergencies, and has focused on activities situated in refugee camps. As it is exceedingly difficult to determine when the emergency phase ends and the chronic phase begins, an evaluation of "lessons learned" should also extend to the chronic phase and the periods of repatriation and resettlement.[8] During these periods, different patterns of illnesses or public health concerns may arise; particularly, mental health concerns or psychosocial illnesses related to the stress associated

with prolonged periods of displacement.[9] However, as shown in the previous discussion of this paper, most of the attention is placed on the emergency phase because of the necessity of meeting essential survival
needs.

Accountability for Humanitarian Relief

In order for best practices to remain the best care accessible under
the varying and trying circumstances of a complex emergency, those
practices need to be routinely monitored and evaluated. The thrust of accountability should be directed to the beneficiaries of aid, rather than to the
donors (Zetter 1999). Accountability should also extend to the local context. Are the public health issues of the displaced reflective of the "normal"
population and, if so, to what extent? It should be incumbent on humanitarian agencies to also evaluate the extent to which the complex emergency
adds to chronic development issues in the local population (Bakewell
2000). Expanding the focus of accountability should serve as a catalyst for
the development of novel public health interventions.

Repeated calls for evaluation of humanitarian assistance have been
raised during the past two decades (Dick and Simmonds 1983; Taylor and
Cuny 1979).

Still, the lack of institutional learning and the need for formal evaluation
remains (Ugalde et al. 1999; Waldman and Martone 1999; Walkup 1997;
Zetter 1999).

This chapter began by discussing "best practices" and how lessons
learned have predominately arisen from personal and/or organizational
experiences. There is a strong need for well designed research relating to
providing public health services in complex emergencies. Results from
these studies can be used as a basis for monitoring and evaluation. Social
scientists can contribute to this research in a variety of ways. For example,
using an analytic framework developed to help NGOs design and evaluate
relief projects (Anderson and Woodrow 1998), conditions surrounding a
crisis situation can be examined from a "needs" or a "vulnerabilities" perspective. Needs refer to immediate requirements for survival or recovery
from a crisis, and tend to represent the areas that public health practitioners traditionally have focused on. In contrast, vulnerabilities refer to long-
term factors that affect the ability of a community to respond to events or
which heighten susceptibility to crisis. Social scientists have experience in
examining the broader social/political/environmental realm of vulnerabilities, as well as identifying capacities, which are described as the strengths
and resources of a community.[10] Although this may seem simplistic and
obvious, the question remains as to why so few humanitarian agencies
seek assistance from social scientists.

Little work has been done on examining the wider, long-term social,
political, and economic impact of health services, both within the refugee

setting and in the host communities. Often health care services in a refugee setting are more elaborate and better equipped than any national health facility. This can engender feelings of resentment, demoralization, and even hostility from local staff that work in neighboring host areas (Cromwell 1988).

As stated throughout this bulletin, blending public health and social science perspectives can strengthen the existing body of knowledge. Often, the practitioners who are providing the hands-on care, and even country-level directors, are too immersed in the day-to-day demands of a complex emergency to question best practices or to engage in research activities that might produce needed information about the people for whom they are providing care. Chapter 4 by MacArthur et al. in this bulletin is one example of an NGO recognizing the additional need for social science expertise in order to improve the health care services offered, as well as the acceptability of such services.

Recommendations

Lessons learned well should generate recommendations for how to improve our public health practices during complex emergencies, including, recognizing the factors that led to the complex emergency, identifying how the emergency has reshaped social organization, and critically appraising how relief efforts may affect social reconstruction after the emergency period ends. Any recommendation given should support full participation by the displaced communities in public health activities, and strive to encourage programs designed to promote self-governance. Recognition of inherent strengths within a displaced community, both by the people themselves and external agencies, is vital to the ability of those people to regain a sense of community. This will provide a basis from which public health efforts can be applied more successfully. Conceptual models of risk, vulnerabilities, and possible solutions need to be continually field tested and refined to see if they are adaptable for all phases of a complex emergency.[11]

In addition to involving the displaced population, essential services, especially health care services, should be integrated whenever possible into the existing services and policies of the host population (Cromwell 1988). Offering assistance to both displaced and host populations in the immediate area of settlement is a cardinal principle of humanitarian practice, but one that is frequently ignored for a variety of reasons (Wilson 1992).

Social scientists and epidemiologists are in an excellent position to argue for increased funding for systematic research and evaluation of relief efforts (Ugalde et al. 1999; Waldman and Martone 1999). Numerous criticisms have been leveled at NGOs and UNHCR over limited assessments, poor management skills, chaos resulting from a plethora of agency responses during larger emergencies, lack of coordination within and among relief agencies, limited human resource planning, and a lack of interest in developing programs that are more sustainable long-term (Lee 1998; Seaman 1999; Walkup 1997; Zetter 1999). In terms of policy analysis, records of the actions of humanitarian agencies are often incomplete, therefore not allowing an analysis of decisions made or of the logic behind the actions of organizations (Seaman 1999). Others have argued that while some of the criticism is valid, there is little empirical evidence to substantiate these claims (Stockton 1998). Addressing research questions and developing routine evaluation and monitoring programs would hopefully promote the incorporation of lessons learned into programmatic planning and agency philosophies, all with a stated goal of improving performance (Banatvala and Zwi 2000; Dick and Simmonds 1983; Walkup 1997).

Social scientists should not stand by passively and wait to be invited as consultants or staff in complex emergency public health programs. Instead, they need to become more proactive, educating humanitarian agencies on the types of expertise they can offer and how they can contribute to the humanitarian relief efforts both from research and programmatic perspectives.

Recently, the Director General of the WHO strongly urged anthropologists to assist epidemiologists in adapting field instruments that have been modeled on western populations (such as in the area of mental health) to more appropriate culture-specific indicators, thus increasing transcultural validity of data and responses (Brundtland 2000).

Increasingly, there is a stated acknowledgement of the role social, cultural, political and economic factors play in individual- and population-based responses to complex emergencies, including how these factors affect relief organizations' definitions of "vulnerable" groups (Davis 1996). The need for qualitative methods expertise and a noted lack of preparation in most NGO staff in this area is also being recognized (Borrel and Salama 1999; Khaw et al. 2000; Young 1999). As well, mixed method approaches using qualitative and quantitative data that incorporate local perspectives are needed to better inform programmatic decisions and policy makers, many of whom lack technical expertise. For example, in the neglected area of preventing human immunodeficiency virus and other sexually transmitted diseases in situations of complex emergencies, qualitative approaches can help in the understanding of the determinants of vulnerability and the identification of groups needing intervention (Khaw et al. 2000).

In spite of the movement forward with this recognition, there is a noticeable gap in the literature. Other than in Brundtland's (2000) editorial, social scientists have not been explicitly identified as the group of professionals who could fill the niche that is currently lacking. This is the critical gap that social science professional advocacy should be addressing. Their varied methods, as described in the introduction of this bulletin, should become staple elements in the information-gathering process. Information from and about the population caught up in the chaos and destruction of a complex emergency is essential if the international community is to do its job competently. Reducing excess preventable morbidity and mortality rates as quickly as possible to their lowest possible level cannot be achieved without a conscious and concerted effort to reach out into the most peripheral segments of the community from the earliest phases of an emergency relief operation.

Notes

Disclaimer. The views expressed within this chapter are solely those of the authors and do not reflect those of the United States Public Health Service.

Acknowledgements. The authors wish to thank Ellen Bahr, M.A., for her assistance in helping to prepare the multiple versions of this manuscript.

1. From the public health perspective, the emergency phase has sometimes been defined as that period during which the number of deaths in a population exceeds 1 per 10,000 per day (normal crude mortality in developing countries is 0.3–0.5 per 10,000 per day). For a variety of reasons, this definition is no longer sufficient. Mortality rates among Kosovar refugees to Macedonia and Albania in spring 1999 and those of Timorese fleeing from East to West Timor in 1999 remained low, but few would not consider both of those acute population displacements to be emergencies.

2. Refugees in Goma were settled on land made of impenetrable volcanic rock. Digging of any kind, whether for latrines or for graves, was almost impossible, and transporting the dead was the only option, from a public health perspective.

3. Complicating this picture is the problem of providing adequate food to the families of combatants who remain in camps. As well, demobilized combatants present another challenge. While not technically refugees, they share many of the characteristics of the displaced and are often thrust into conditions of stark poverty upon demobilization (Green 2000).

4. As a general rule, water intended for consumption should contain less than 10 fecal coliforms per 100 milliliters.

5. For an excellent account of the consequences of cultural misunderstandings between a resettled Laotian refugee family and a small, county hospital, we refer readers to Anne Fadiman's *The Spirit Catches You and You Fall Down: A Hmong Child, Her American Doctors, and the Collision of Two Cultures* (1977).

6. An excellent guide on using participatory approaches in a field situation is published by Catholic Relief Services, entitled *Rapid Rural Appraisal (RRA) and Participatory Rural Appraisal (PRA): A Manual for CRS Field Workers and Partners,* by Karen Schoonmaker Freudenberger. Refer to chapter 1 of this bulletin for a further discussion of participatory approaches and citations for additional information on these methods.

7. The role of "community leaders" should be examined carefully when the interests of marginalized populations are being presented by individuals outside of those populations. For example, there is a predominance of male decision makers on the community level. The perspectives of these men may differ radically from women's interests (Palmer et al. 1999). As well, the "elite" leaders of refugee populations (those who are bilingual and have higher levels of education) may not be adequately representing the interests of the poorest, more rural majority segments of the displaced populations (Sommers 1995).

8. There are additional forms of settlement, such as scheme-settled or self-settled refugees or internally displaced persons (IDP), whose concerns are not addressed in this essay. Little has been done to document the public health needs of these populations or to investigate health care accessibility. As well, the impact of such settlements on the host population's ability to access health care has not been explored much.

9. For an excellent discussion of the public health issues, as well as attention to the social needs, seen during repatriation or resettlement, we refer readers to part 4 of *Refugee Health: An Approach to Emergency Situations* (MSF 1997:295–306).

10. Social/political assessments related to disaster and development frequently use overlapping terminologies. For example, Cernea (2000) uses the term *risk* to highlight social and economic factors that cause impoverishment through resettlement (model is currently being expanded to include refugee situations as well). Vulnerability assessments can also

refer to procedures used to assess vulnerability to natural disasters. *Needs assessments* has been used in community-based public health projects as a method to identify and prioritize health concerns or programmatic interests.

11. Two models that have been referred to in this chapter are the "Impoverishment Risk and Reconstruction Model for Resettling Displaced Populations" (Cernea 2000) and the analytic framework for "Vulnerabilities and Capacities Analysis" (Anderson and Woodrow 1998).

References Cited

Anderson, Mary, and Peter Woodrow
    1998   Rising from the Ashes: Development Strategies in Times of Disaster. Boulder: Lynne Rienne Publishers, Inc.
Bakewell, Oliver
    2000   Uncovering Local Perspectives on Humanitarian Assistance and Its Outcomes. Disasters 24:103–116.
Baquet, Sophie, François Wuillaume, Kathia Van Egmond, and Felicitas Ibanez
    2000   Pellagra Outbreak in Kuito, Angola. Lancet 355:1822–1830.
Banatvala, Nicholas, and Anthony Zwi
    2000   Public Health and Humanitarian Interventions: Developing the Evidence Base. British Medical Journal 321:101–105.
Bhattacharyya, Karabi, and John Murray
    2000   Community Assessment and Planning for Maternal and Child Health Programs: A Participatory Approach in Ethiopia. Human Organization 59:255–266.
Borrel, Annalies, and Peter Salama
    1999   Public Nutrition from an Approach to a Discipline: Concern's Nutrition Case Studies in Complex Emergencies. Disasters 23:326–342.
Brundtland, Gro Harlem
    2000   Editorial. Mental Health of Refugees, Internally Displaced Persons and Other Populations Affected by Conflict. Acta Psychiatry Scandanavia 102:159–161.
Burkle, Frederick M.
    1999   Fortnightly Review. Lessons Leant and Future Expectations of Complex Emergencies. British Medical Journal 319:422–426.
Centers for Disease Control and Prevention
    1990   Update: Health and Nutritional Profiles of Refugees–Ethiopia, 1998–1990. Morbidity and Mortality Weekly Report 39:707–709,715–718.
    1992   Famine-Affected, Refugee, and Displaced populations: Recommendations for Public Health Issues. Morbidity and Mortality Weekly Report 41(RR–13):1–25.
Cernea, Michael
    2000   Risks, Safeguards, and Reconstruction: A Model for Population Displacement and Resettlement. In Risks and Reconstruction. Experience of Resettlers and Refugees. Michael Chernea and Christopher McDowell, eds. Pp. 11–55. Washington, DC: The World Bank.
Cromwell, Godfrey
    1988   Note on the Role of Expatriate Administrators in Agency-Assisted Refugee Programs. Journal of Refugee Studies 1:297–307.
Davis, Austen P.
    1996   Targeting the Vulnerable in Emergency Situations: Who Is Vulnerable? The Lancet 348:868–871.
Desenclos, Jean-Claude, Angela Berry, R. Padt, Basra Farah, Claire Segala, and A. M. Nabil
    1989   Epidemiological Patterns of Scurvy among Ethiopian Refugees. Bulletin of the World Health Organization 67(3):309–316.
Dick, Bruce, and Stephanie Simmonds
    1983   Refugee Health Care: Similar but Different? Disasters 7:291–303.
Fadiman, Anne
    1997   The Spirit Catches You and You Fall Down: A Hmong Child, Her American Doctors, and the Collision of Two Cultures. New York: The Noonday Press.
Freudenberger, Karen Schoonmaker
    1999   Rapid Rural Appraisal (RRA) and Participatory Rural Appraisal (PRA): A Manual for CRS Field Workers and Partners. Balitmore: Catholic Relief Services.

Goma Epidemiology Group
  1995 Public Health Impact of Rwandan Refugee Crisis: What Happened in Goma, Zaire, in July, 1994? Lancet 345(8946):339–344.
Green, Reginald Herbold
  2000 Food Security in Refuge and Return: Some Aspects of Entitlements, Markets, and Modalities. In Risks and Reconstruction. Experience of Resettlers and Refugees. Michael Chernea and Christopher McDowell, eds. Pp. 253–292. Washington, DC: The World Bank.
Harrell-Bond, Barbara, Eftihia Voutira, and Mark Leopold
  1992 Counting the Refugees: Gifts, Givers, Patrons, and Clients. Journal of Refugee Studies 5:205–225.
Heuveline, Patrick
  1998 Between One and Three Million: Towards the Demographic Reconstruction of a Decade of Cambodian History (1970–1979). Population Studies 52:49–65.
Jaspars, Susanne, and Jeremy Shoham
  1999 Targeting the Vulnerable: A Review of the Necessity and Feasibility of Targeting Vulnerable Households. Disasters 23:359–372.
Khaw, Adrian J., Peter Salama, Brent Burkholder, and Timothy J. Dondero
  2000 HIV Risk and Prevention in Emergency-Affected Populations: A Review. Disasters 24:181–197.
Landman, Jacqueline
  1999 Food Aid in Emergencies: A Case for Wheat? Proceedings of the Nutrition Society 58:355–361.
Lee, Kelley
  1998 Finding a Better Way for Humanitarian Action: Creating a Global Institutional Framework. A Rejoinder. Security Dialogue 29:151–155.
Magan, Ahmed, Mohammed Warsame, Abdikamal Ali-Salad, and Michael Toole
  1983 An Outbreak of Scurvy in Somalia Refugee Camps. Disasters 7:94–97.
Malfait, Philippe, Alain Moren, J. C. Dillon, A. Brodel, Genevieve Begkoyian, Marc Etchegorry, Grace Malenga, and Peter Hakewill
  1993 An Outbreak of Pellagra Related to Changes in Dietary Niacin among Mozambican Refugees in Malawi. International Journal of Epidemiology 22(3):504–511.
Mason, John, Stuart Gillespie, Graeme Clugston, and Peter Greaves
  1992 Misconceptions on Nutrition of Refugees. Lancet 340:1354.
Médecins Sans Frontères
  1997 Refugee Health: An Approach to Emergency Situations. London: MacMillan.
Palmer, Celia A., Louisiana Lush, and Anthony B. Zwi
  1999 The Emerging International Policy Agenda for Reproductive Health Services in Conflict Settings. Social Science and Medicine 49:1689–1703.
Physicians for Human Rights
  1999 War Crimes in Kosovo. Boston: Physicians for Human Rights.
Reed, Barbara, and Jean-Paul Habicht
  1998 Sales of Food Aid as a Sign of Distress, Not Excess. Lancet 351:128–130.
Seaman, John
  1999 Malnutrition in Emergencies: How Can We Do Better and Where Do the Responsibilities Lie? Disasters 23:306–315.
Sommers, Marc
  1995 Representing Refugees: The Role of Elites in Burundi Refugee Society. Disasters 19:19–25.
Sphere Project
  2000 Humanitarian Charter and Minimum Standards in Disaster Response. Oxford: Oxford Publishing.
Stockton, Nicholas
  1998 In Defense of Humanitarianism. Disasters 22:352–360.
Taylor, Alan, and Frederick Cuny
  1979 The Evaluation of Humanitarian Assistance. Disasters 3:37–42.
Toole, Michael, and Ronald Waldman
  1990 Prevention of Excess Mortality in Refugee and Displaced Populations in Developing Countries. Journal of the American Medical Association 263:3296–3302.

Ugalde, Antonio, Patricia Richards, and Anthony Zwi
    1999 Health Consequences of War and Political Violence. Encyclopedia of Violence, Peace and Conflict 2:103–121.
Waldman, Ronald, Alfred Bartlett III, Carlos C. Campbell, and Richard W. Steketee
    1996 Overcoming Remaining Barriers: The Pathway to Survival. Arlington, VA: BASICS.
Waldman, Ronald, and Gerald Martone
    1999 Public Health and Complex Emergencies: New Issues, New Conditions. American Journal of Public Health 89:1483–1485.
Walkup, Mark
    1997 Policy Dysfunction in Humanitarian Organizations: The Role of Coping Strategies, Institutions, and Organizational Culture. Journal of Refugee Studies 10:37–60.
Webb, Patrick, and Anuradha Harinarayan
    1999 A Measure of Uncertainty: The Nature of Vulnerability and Its Relationship to Malnutrition. Disasters 23:292–305.
Werner, David, and David Sanders
    1997 Questioning the Solution: the Politics of Primary health Care. Palo Alto, CA: Healthwrights.
Wilson, Ken B.
    1992 Enhancing Refugees' Own Food Acquisition Strategies. Journal of Refugee Studies 5:226–246.
World Food Program and United Nations High Commissioner for Refugees
    1997 WFP/UNHCR Guidelines for Estimating Food and Nutritional Needs in Emergencies. Geneva: World Food Program and United Nations High Commissioner for Refugees.
World Health Organization
    1999 Inventory of Applied Health Research in Emergency Settings. 1st ed. Geneva: Department of Emergency and Humanitarian Action.
Young, Helen
    1999 Public Nutrition in Emergencies: An Overview of Debates, Dilemmas and Decision-Making. Disasters 23:277–291.
Zetter, Roger
    1999 International Perspectives on Refugee Assistance. In Refugees: Perspectives on the Experience of Forced Migration. Alastair Ager, ed. Pp. 46–82. London: Pinter.

ABOUT THE CONTRIBUTORS

PETER B. BLOLAND is an epidemiologist assigned to the Malaria Epidemiology Branch, Division of Parasitic Diseases, Centers for Disease Control and Prevention, Atlanta, GA. He received his Doctor of Veterinary Medicine and Masters in Preventive Veterinary Medicine degrees from the University of California at Davis. He is a member of the Roll Back Malaria Technical Resource Network on Malaria Control in Complex Emergencies. His refugee field experience includes Zaire, Eritrea, and Tanzania. He has published papers in *Lancet* and *Refuge* regarding complex emergencies and is a contributing author to an interagency handbook on malaria control in the context of complex emergencies, being published by UNCHR and WHO. His current research interests in regard to complex emergencies include antimalarial drug resistance, general malaria control and prevention strategies.

SANDRA DUDLEY recently completed her doctoral thesis in Social Anthropology at the University of Oxford and will be assuming the post of temporary lecturer at the University of East Anglia (UK). Her dissertation is entitled "Displacement and Identity: Karenni Refugees in Thailand." Field experience includes Burma (Myanmar), as well as Thailand. She has publications on Karenni refugees in *Urgent Anthropological and Ethnological Research* (UNESCO), *Forced Migration Review,* and *Cultural Survival Quarterly.* She is presently co-editing (with Edith Bowles) a book on Burmese identities in displacement and exile, as well as a book on anthropological approaches to dress and textiles in Burma (with Elizabeth Dell). Current research interests include cultural and political identities in displacement, health and illness, memory and ideas of "home," and material culture.

SUZANNE FUSTUKIAN is Senior Lecturer in International Health at the Centre for International Health Studies, Queen Margaret University College in Edinburgh. Prior to this, she was a Research Fellow in Conflict and Health in the Health Policy Unit at the London School of Hygiene and Tropical Medicine, London, UK, undertaking multidisciplinary research on the impact of conflict on health and post-conflict health policy. She has a Masters degree in Social Policy and Planning in Developing Countries from the London School of Economics. She has field experience in a number of countries: Tanzania, Namibia, India, Kenya, and the Occupied Palestinian

Territories. She is co-editor of a forthcoming book *Health Policy in a Globalising World: Crossing Boundaries,* published by Cambridge University Press, and has written a number of papers with Anthony Zwi around conflict and health. Major research interests include health and social policy in "post"-conflict environments; urban health, particularly in relation to the informal sector and marginalized groups; equity; civil society and its role in governance; nongovernmental organizations (NGOs), and globalization and its consequences for national/regional stability.

JOHN R. MacARTHUR is a medical epidemiologist assigned to the Malaria Epidemiology Branch, Division of Parasitic Diseases, Centers for Disease Control and Prevention, Atlanta, GA. He received his medical degree from Georgetown University and his Master's of Public Health degree from Johns Hopkins University. He completed residencies in Family and Community Medicine at the University of California at San Francisco/San Francisco General Hospital and Preventive Medicine at Johns Hopkins. He also completed a François-Xavier Bagnoud corresponding fellowship in Health and Human Rights at Harvard University. He has worked with refugees from Africa, Asia, Central America, and the Middle East and was Clinical Health Manager for the International Rescue Committee on the Thai/Burmese border. He has co-authored an article on malaria control in complex emergencies in *Refuge.* Currently, his research interests include evaluation of antimalarial drug resistance, malaria drug policy, and malaria control in complex humanitarian emergencies.

LUCIA ANN McSPADDEN is Senior Research Fellow of the Life and Peace Institute (LPI), an international peace research institute associated with the World Council of Churches. Currently based in California, she was the Research Director for LPI in Sweden for five years. She received her Ph.D. in Cultural Anthropology from the University of Utah. A Fellow of the American Anthropological Association (AAA) and of the Society for Applied Anthropology, she is a founding member of both the AAA's Committee on Refugees and Immigrants (CORI) and of the International Association for the Study of Forced Migration and was Co-chair of the AAA's Committee for Human Rights. For the past 20 years she has conducted research on refugee issues and has applied field experience with refugee communities, including working with resettled refugees in the US, as well as in refugee camps in Eritrea and Kenya. She is author of *Negotiating the Terrain: Conflict, Control and Compromise in the Repatriation of Eritrean Refugees* (Life and Peace Institute) and co-editor of *Negotiating Power and Place at the Margins: Selected Papers on Refugees and Immigrants, vol. VII* (American Anthropological Association), and *Women, Violence and Nonviolent Change* (World Council of Churches), as well as author of numerous articles on refugees and human rights, including papers in the African volume in the Greenwood Press series on Endangered Peoples,

Power, Ethics, and Human Rights: Anthropological Studies of Refugee Research and Action (Rowman and Littlefield Publishers, Inc.), *The End of the Refugee Cycle? Refugee Repatriation and Reconstruction* (Berghahn Press), *The Future of the United Nations Systems* (UN University Press), *The Journal of Refugee Studies, Refuge,* and *International Migration Review.* Currently, she is directing a multinational study on the role of NGOs in the repatriation of refugees. Her present research focus is a longitudinal investigation of the repatriation and resettlement of refugees from the Horn of Africa.

RONALD WALDMAN is currently the Director of the Program on Forced Migration and Health and Professor of Clinical Public Health at the Heilbrunn Center for Population and Family Health, the Mailman School of Public Health of Columbia University. He received his medical degree from the University of Geneva, Switzerland, and has a Master's in Public Health degree from the Johns Hopkins University. He has years of applied public health experience in refugee settings in Somalia, Iraq, Bosnia, Zaire, Rwanda, Burundi, and Albania. In addition to operational research, he currently teaches an MPH course and directs a short course for humanitarian relief workers entitled "Public Health in Complex Emergencies," which has been taught in Bosnia, Thailand, and Uganda. He has written extensively in the area of public health and complex emergencies and has publications in *The American Journal of Public Health, Lancet, Journal of the American Medical Association, Bulletin of the World Health Organization, Tuberculosis,* and *Journal of Pediatrics.* His research interests include the development and implementation of health policy in complex emergencies.

HOLLY ANN WILLIAMS is an anthropologist assigned to the Malaria Epidemiology Branch, Division of Parasitic Diseases, Centers for Disease Control and Prevention, Atlanta, Ga. She received a Ph.D. in medical and cultural anthropology from the University of Florida and has a clinical specialty in pediatric nursing, with a Master's in Nursing from the University of Washington. During 1988 she was a study fellow in the Refugee Studies Programme at Oxford University, England. She is a member of the AAA's Committee on Refugee and Immigrants (CORI). She has public health, clinical, and research experience in Thailand, Sudan, Tanzania, and Zambia, working with refugees in camps, self-settled refugees and internally displaced persons. She is also a member of the Roll Back Malaria Technical Resource Network on Malaria Control in Complex Emergencies and is a contributing author to an interagency handbook on malaria control in the context of complex emergencies, being published by UNCHR and WHO. She has authored or co-authored papers relating to refugee studies in the journals *Human Organization and Refuge,* as well as the edited volume *Selected Papers on Refugee Issues: vol. II* (American Anthropology Association). Currently, her research interests include malaria control in complex emergencies, the process of decision making as it relates to the formulation and implementation of national antimalarial drug treatment policies, and sociobehavioral issues related to malaria control.

ANTHONY B. ZWI has headed the Health Policy Unit at the London School of Hygiene and Tropical Medicine since 1997. He obtained his medical degree and postgraduate diplomas in occupational health and tropical medicine from South Africa, his country of origin. He subsequently trained in epidemiology, public health, and international health at the London School of Hygiene and Tropical Medicine, and in the United Kingdom national health service. He has a long-standing interest in how conflict impacts on health and health systems. He is currently promoting the establishment of a network to adapt and transfer analytic tools and response strategies between countries emerging from major periods of conflict. He is committed to developing and advocating for mechanisms whereby affected communities can make their voices heard, policy-makers and the policies they promote can be made more accountable, and academic-NGO partnerships ensure that lessons are learned and mistakes not repeated in humanitarian and development contexts. He has worked in South Africa and undertaken research in Cambodia, Ethiopia, Palestine, Croatia, and Kosovo. He currently serves as a Senior Editor for Health Policy for Social Science and Medicine and has published in the areas of complex emergencies and conflict and health, with papers in *British Medical Journal, Disasters, Encyclopedia of Violence, Peace, and Conflict; Journal of International Development;* and *Social Science and Medicine.* In addition, he has co-edited *War and Hunger: Rethinking International Responses to Complex Emergencies* (Zed Press) with Joanna Macrae.